Core Concepts in Embryology

Core Concepts in Embryology

Alexander Sandra, Ph.D.

Professor of Anatomy, University of Iowa College of Medicine, Iowa City, Iowa

Illustrations by William J. Coons, B.F.A.

Lippincott - Raven

PUBLISHERS

Philadelphia • New York

Library of Congress Cataloging-in-Publication Data

Sandra, Alexander.
    Core concepts in embryology / Alexander Sandra ; illustrations by
William J. Coons.
      p. cm.
    Includes index.
    ISBN 0-316-01884-8
    1. Embryology, Human.   I. Title.
    [DNLM: 1. Embryology.   QS 604 S219c 1997]
QM601.S235   1997
612.6′4 — dc20
DNLM/DLC
for Library of Congress   96-35595
                                       CIP

Printed in the United States of America

VICTOR GRAPHICS, INC.

Production Services: Textbook Writers Associates, Inc.

Copyeditor: Beverly Miller

Indexer: Michael Loo

Designer: Linda Dana Willis

Cover Design: Hannus Design Associates

Contents

Preface

With the tremendous explosion of new medical knowledge, basic science curricula in the professional health care fields have increasingly faced pressure to simultaneously find room to accommodate this new knowledge, reduce exposure to "classical" disciplines, integrate information across traditional lines, and make the subject matter more clinically relevant. A good example of this may be found in the area of embryology. Modern cell and molecular biology are now unraveling many of the age-old problems that formed the cornerstone of classical embryology. Problems such as the mechanisms involved in primary induction and pattern formation are no longer intractable issues limited to phenomenologic description. Ironically, however, the introduction of such exciting new knowledge virtually ensures the expansion of the curriculum since it cannot profitably be discussed at the introductory level outside the context of basic embryologic processes.

Core Concepts in Embryology is an attempt to provide basic embryologic information. The book may be used alone, as in the one-semester hour course given to medical students at the University of Iowa, or in conjunction with supplemental material emphasizing more detailed or experimental approaches. The intent is to provide not a comprehensive outline but an illustrated, quickly read narrative of the key events generally presented in an abbreviated course. It is hoped that this book will also serve as an introduction to basic human embryology for students in the other professional fields of health care and as a useful review for comprehensive examinations given well after students' formal exposure to human embryology.

A. S.

Early Human Development

1 / *Major Events in Fertilization*

The process of fertilization in the human is a complex multistage event that normally occurs in the uterine tube. The egg, surrounded by granulosa cells making up the corona radiata, is fertilized as a secondary oocyte during metaphase of its second meiotic division. Thus one polar body, itself undergoing its second meiosis, is found between the oocyte and the zona pellucida, the dense extracellular matrix layer between the oocyte and corona radiata. This small space is called the perivitelline space. ■ **Fig. A** ■

As the spermatozoa approach the oocyte, they must penetrate a cellular barrier, the corona radiata, as well as a noncellular barrier, the zone pellucida, before they actually contact the oocyte membrane. This penetration is facilitated by the breakdown of a specialized membrane-bound organelle in the head of the spermatozoa known as the acrosome. The acrosome contains a variety of proteolytic enzymes, which are released during this phase of fertilization. ■ **Fig. B** ■

The next phase of fertilization is characterized by the transient fusion of the plasma membranes of the oocytes and the spermatozoan and an accompanying series of biochemical and physiologic changes in the newly fertilized egg. Once the spermatozoan is incorporated within the cytoplasm of the oocyte, the densely packed chromatin material in the head of the spermatozoan undergoes decondensation as the male and female pronuclei approach one another. ■ **Fig. C** ■ Homologous chromosomes align to form the first mitotic division plane of the newly fertilized egg, or zygote. ■ **Fig. D** ■

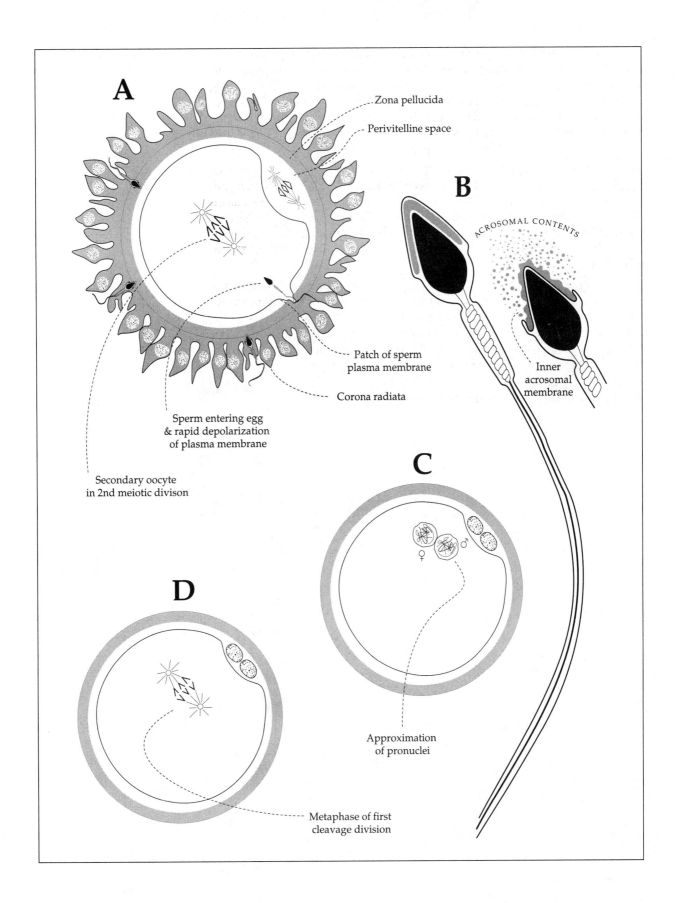

A

Zona pellucida

Perivitelline space

B

ACROSOMAL CONTENTS

Inner acrosomal membrane

Patch of sperm plasma membrane

Corona radiata

Sperm entering egg & rapid depolarization of plasma membrane

Secondary oocyte in 2nd meiotic divison

C

♀ ♂

D

Approximation of pronuclei

Metaphase of first cleavage division

2 / Early Cleavage and Blastocyst Formation

The first week of human embryologic development occurs in suspension within the uterine tube and uterus. The zygote undergoes a series of asynchronous mitotic divisions to form a loosely adhering group of similar cells known as the morula. ■ **Fig. A** ■ Each cell division takes about a day, and the individual cells at this stage are called blastomeres. As division proceeds, the cells become smaller, and the entire mass of cells is still surrounded by the zona pellucida. The perivitelline space becomes quite pronounced.

Late in the morula stage, about the middle of the first week after fertilization, the blastomeres become much more closely adherent to one another, a process called compaction. Soon afterward, the formerly solid ball of cells develops a fluid-filled internal space, the blastocele. ■ **Fig. B** ■ The embryo is now called a blastocyst. As development continues, the blastocele expands enormously. ■ **Fig. C** ■ This process results in the establishment of two kinds of cells in the blastocyst: the trophoblast cells, which form a single external cell layer, and the inner cell mass, a group of cells within the trophoblast located at one pole of the blastocyst. This early segregation of two cell types is the basis for all future development. The cells of the trophoblast will differentiate further to form structures associated with, but not part of, the embryo. The inner cell mass will give rise to embryo proper. Note that at the blastocyst stage, the zona pellucida has been sloughed off and no longer surrounds the embryo.

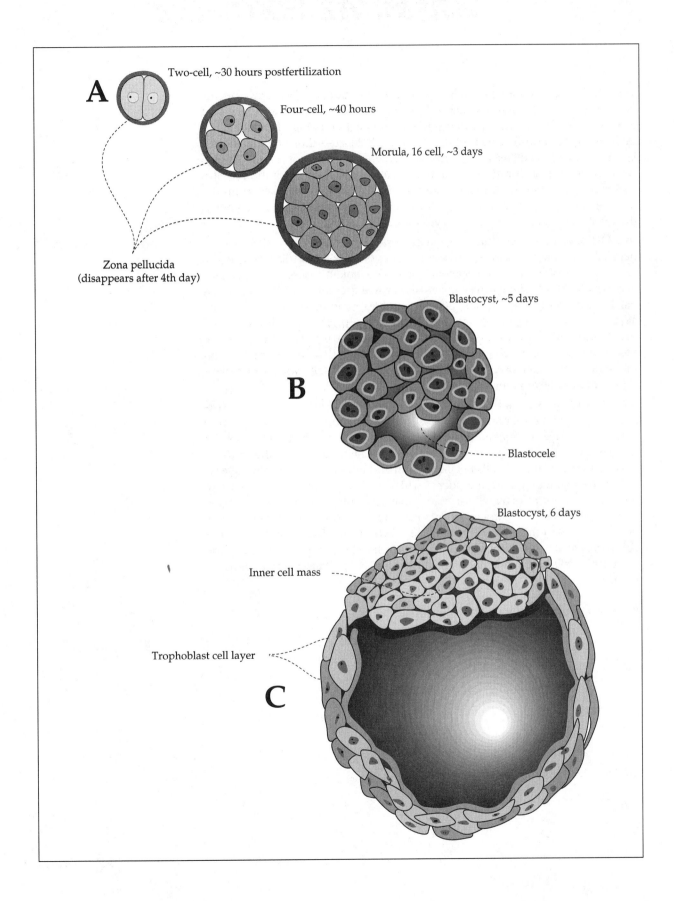

A — Two-cell, ~30 hours postfertilization

Four-cell, ~40 hours

Morula, 16 cell, ~3 days

Zona pellucida
(disappears after 4th day)

B — Blastocyst, ~5 days

Blastocele

Blastocyst, 6 days

Inner cell mass

Trophoblast cell layer

C

3 / Implantation and Bilaminar Disc Formation

Toward the end of the first week following fertilization, the blastocyst undergoes two fundamental developmental processes. In the first of these, depicted in ■ **Fig. A** ■, the blastocyst attaches to the endometrial lining of the uterus to initiate implantation. The cells of the polar trophoblast — those that reside adjacent to the inner cell mass — invade first. As they do, many of these cells fuse with one another to form a syncytium, or a cellular mass in which the cells are no longer separated by plasma membranes. This syncytiotrophoblast forms the leading edge of the invasion. By contrast, cells of the trophoblast, which retain their cellularity, are known as the cytotrophoblast. ■ **Fig. B** ■

In ■ **Fig. B** ■, the second fundamental process is observed. The cells of the inner cell mass have re-formed to produce a two-cell layered disc. Hence, the second week of human development can be conveniently described as the bilaminar disc stage. The two cell layers are termed the epiblast (for the columnar layer nearer to the invading polar trophoblast) and the hypoblast (for the adjacent squamous-cuboidal layer). Note that this reorganization has occurred before the entire blastocyst has been incorporated within the stroma of the uterus. In addition, observe that a cavity has formed between the epiblast and the underlying trophoblast and is lined by cells in continuity with the epiblast. This is the primitive amniotic cavity.

As invasion continues ■ **Fig. C** ■, the former blastocyst cavity no longer exists and is replaced by the primitive yolk sac or exocoelomic cavity. This structure is lined by a layer of squamous epithelial cells continuous with the hypoblast known as Hauser's membrane. Between this membrane and the cytotrophoblast, a new layer of cells begins to form and rapidly expands. This layer is called the extraembryonic mesoderm. These cells are embedded in a loose reticular network of extracellular matrix that gives this layer its distinct histologic appearance. The extraembryonic mesoderm is so named because it will not contribute to the mesoderm of the embryo proper. Its origin, however, is controversial. It is not clear whether it arises from cells migrating out of the epiblast, from cells of the neighboring cytotrophoblast or Hauser's membrane, or both.

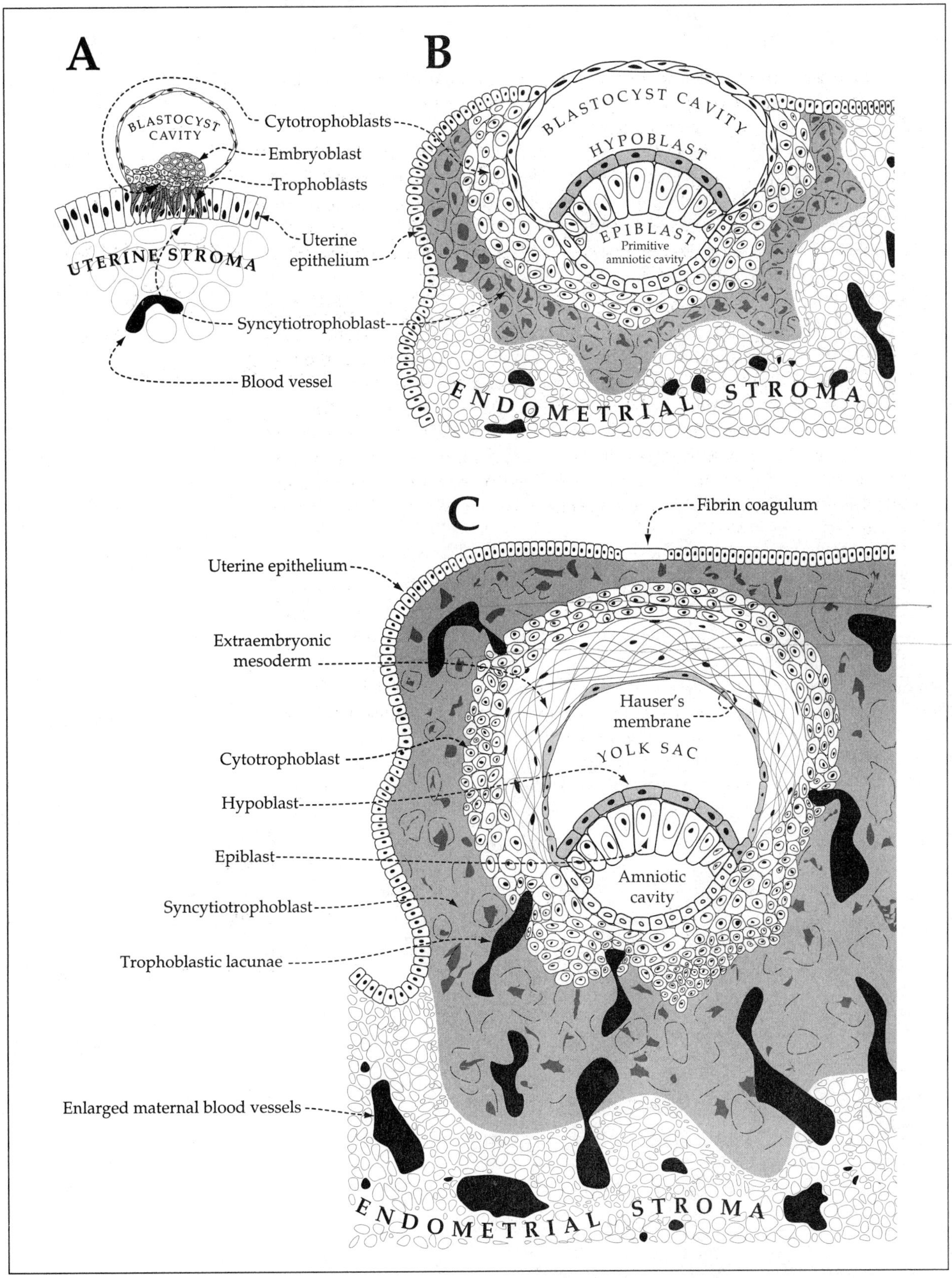

A

- Cytotrophoblasts
- Embryoblast
- Trophoblasts
- Uterine epithelium
- Syncytiotrophoblast
- Blood vessel

BLASTOCYST CAVITY

UTERINE STROMA

B

BLASTOCYST CAVITY

HYPOBLAST

EPIBLAST
Primitive amniotic cavity

ENDOMETRIAL STROMA

C

- Fibrin coagulum
- Uterine epithelium
- Extraembryonic mesoderm
- Cytotrophoblast
- Hypoblast
- Epiblast
- Syncytiotrophoblast
- Trophoblastic lacunae
- Enlarged maternal blood vessels

Hauser's membrane

YOLK SAC

Amniotic cavity

ENDOMETRIAL STROMA

4 / Development of the Secondary Yolk Sac and Early Chorion

As the extraembryonic mesoderm continues to proliferate and the trophoblast expands, fluid-filled spaces, or lacunae, appear in the space occupied by the extraembryonic mesoderm. Note that the primitive yolk sac is lined externally by cells of the extraembryonic mesoderm. Concurrently, the primitive yolk sac undergoes a transformation in which cells of the hypoblast continue to proliferate and appear to displace the primitive yolk sac. The former primary yolk sac is pinched off, and remnants of this transient structure are incorporated into the wall of the extraembryonic mesoderm. ■ **Fig. A** ■ The new yolk sac resulting from this pinching-off process is called the secondary or definitive yolk sac.

In ■ **Fig. B** ■, all of the spaces of the extraembryonic mesoderm have coalesced to form a continuous extraembryonic coelom, or mesoderm-lined space. Note that the extraembryonic mesoderm lines the outer aspect of the amnion and the definitive yolk sac. It also forms the cellular bridge between the developing embryo and the trophoblast. This is the early connecting stalk, which will develop into the umbilical cord. The extraembryonic coelom may now be termed the chorionic cavity. The chorion itself, then, comprises the extraembryonic mesoderm surrounding this cavity and the trophoblast, both cytotrophoblast and syncytiotrophoblast, which peripherally surrounds the extraembryonic mesoderm.

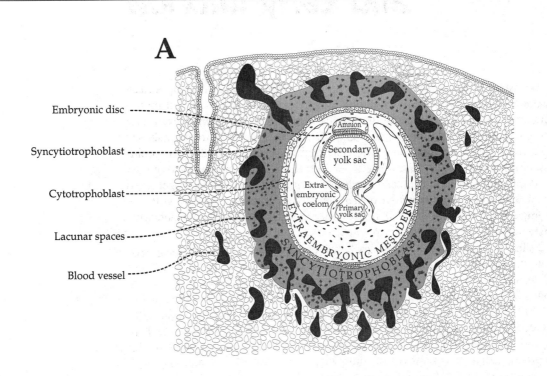

A

Embryonic disc

Syncytiotrophoblast

Cytotrophoblast

Lacunar spaces

Blood vessel

Amnion

Secondary yolk sac

Extra-embryonic coelom

Primary yolk sac

EXTRAEMBRYONIC MESODERM

SYNCYTIOTROPHOBLAST

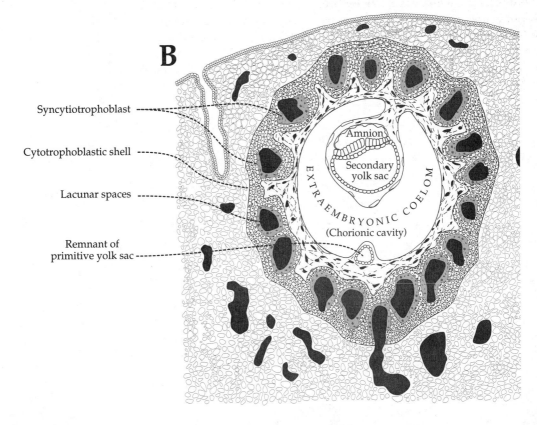

B

Syncytiotrophoblast

Cytotrophoblastic shell

Lacunar spaces

Remnant of primitive yolk sac

Amnion

Secondary yolk sac

EXTRAEMBRYONIC COELOM

(Chorionic cavity)

5 / In Vitro Fertilization: Embryology and Methodology

Within the past two decades, human in vitro fertilization has become a routine procedure. There are several variations of this technique, all of which begin with the surgical removal of maturing eggs from the ovary of the donor following superovulation by hormonal stimulation. Once the eggs are collected, they are placed in a culture medium formulated to support their maturation to the second meiotic metaphase stage. A capacitated sperm concentrate is introduced into the medium to initiate fertilization. At this point, the fertilized eggs are allowed to develop from early cleavage stages up to the blastocyst stage and implanted in the uterine wall. This is known as in vitro fertilization embryo transfer (IVF-ET). Alternatively, in vitro fertilized embryos at the zygote or pronuclear stage of development may be introduced into the uterine tube from where they would be transported naturally to the uterine wall as they continue cell division and blastocyst formation. This variation of in vitro fertilization is known as zygote interfallopian transfer (ZIFT) or pronuclear stage transfer (PROST). Finally, the surgically retrieved eggs may mature in vitro and be introduced into the uterine tube in the presence of capacitated sperm. Fertilization and all subsequent development takes place in its natural environment. In this procedure, gametes rather than embryos are transferred; hence this procedure is termed gamete interfallopian transfer (GIFT).

More sophisticated specialized techniques have been developed in the area of in vitro fertilization. For example, single sperm cells can be introduced in eggs by micropipette after creating holes in the zona pellucida. This is known as zona drilling and can be followed up by either the IVF-ET or ZIFT/PROST procedure.

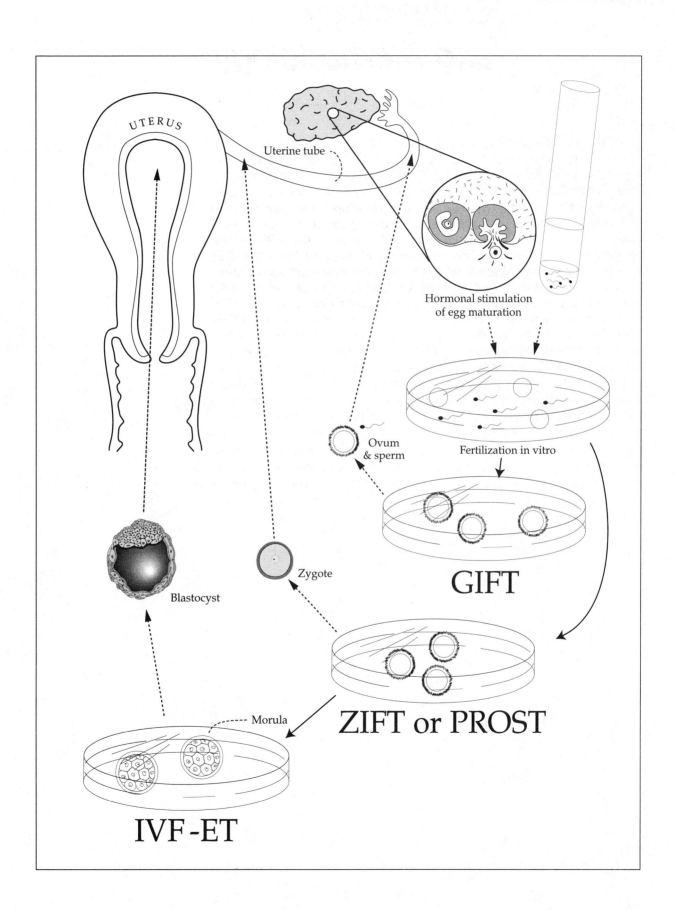

UTERUS

Uterine tube

Hormonal stimulation
of egg maturation

Fertilization in vitro

Ovum
& sperm

GIFT

Zygote

ZIFT or PROST

Blastocyst

Morula

IVF-ET

6 / *Gastrulation*

The end of the second week and beginning of the third week of development is characterized by the process of gastrulation. By this event, the bilaminar disc, comprising a hypoblast layer and overlying epiblast layer, is transformed into a three-layered disc. Hence, the third week after fertilization may be thought of as the trilaminar disc stage of human development. At the beginning of gastrulation, the bilaminar disc is an oval-shaped structure. The future caudal end of the embryo develops a shallow furrow in the midline of the disc known as the primitive streak. The cranial, or head end, of the streak comprises a tuft of cells called the primitive knot or Hensen's node.■ **Fig. A** ■

In ■ **Fig. B** ■, cells of the epiblast migrate toward the primitive streak and involute to form a third layer of cells residing between the epiblast and hypoblast. These loosely organized, migrating cells form the intraembryonic mesoderm. This mesoderm takes a position separating the epiblast and hypoblast in all regions of the former bilaminar disc, with the notable exception of a small midline area at the rostral end of the embryo. This cranial area of adherent epiblast and hypoblast is the **prochordal plate.** The mesoderm, which takes a position cranially in line with the primitive streak, forms a rodlike cell column known as the notochord. After intraembryonic mesoderm formation, the primitive streak regresses and normally disappears.

Toward the end of the third week, the stage is set for the laying down of the body form. The intraembryonic mesoderm in the dorsal midline immediately rostral to the primitive knot forms a cylindrical rod of cells called the notochord. Looking down at the dorsal aspect of the embryo at this time reveals an elongated trilaminar disc in which the epiblast, now properly termed ectoderm, is just starting the process of forming the early central nervous system.■ **Fig. C** ■

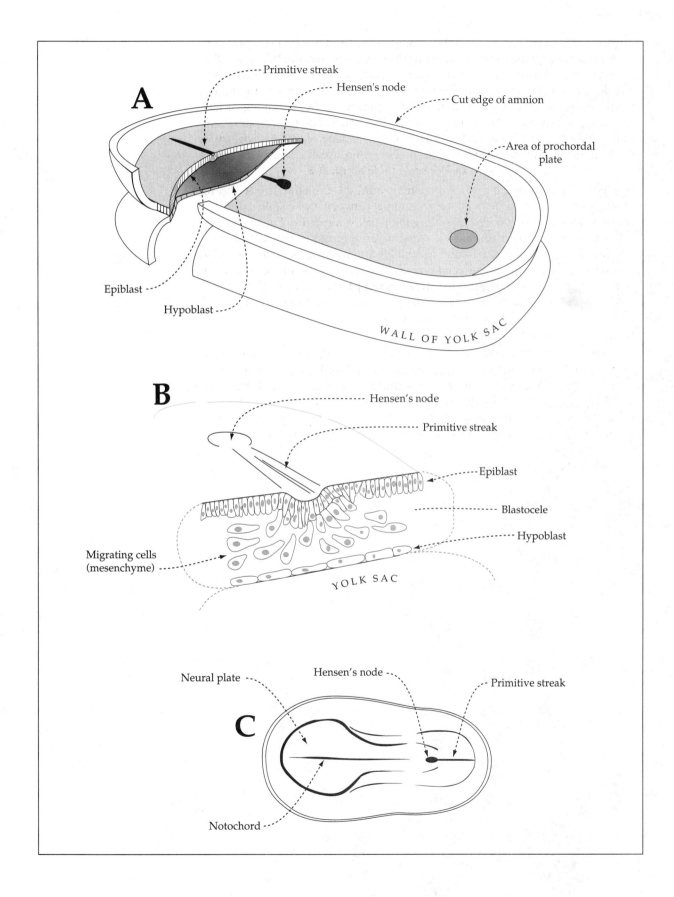

A

Primitive streak

Hensen's node

Cut edge of amnion

Area of prochordal plate

Epiblast

Hypoblast

WALL OF YOLK SAC

B

Hensen's node

Primitive streak

Epiblast

Blastocele

Hypoblast

Migrating cells (mesenchyme)

YOLK SAC

C

Neural plate

Hensen's node

Primitive streak

Notochord

II

Establishment of Body Form

7 / Neural Folding and Formation of the Neural Tube

The development of body form involves processes by which the external appearance of the embryo is first transformed from a flattened disc into a cylindrical tube. ■ **Figs. A–C** ■ The surface ectoderm along the midline of the embryo thickens to form the neural plate. Early in the fourth week of development, the edges of this specialized ectoderm fuse in the midline as its central portion sinks ventrally within the space occupied by the intraembryonic mesoderm, thereby forming a tube. Looking down at the embryo with the amnion removed it is clear that this fusion process begins in the middle of the embryo and then proceeds both cranially and caudally. See ■ **Fig. B** ■ The last parts of the neural tube to fuse are at the caudal end, the posterior neuropore, and the cranial end, the anterior neuropore. See ■ **Fig. C** ■ In a cross-section representation, the transformation of the neural plate to form sequentially a fold, a groove, and finally a tube is evident. ■ **Fig. D** ■ Note that the notochord is positioned immediately ventral to the developing neural tube. Also, migrating cells found dorsolaterally to the neural tube make their first appearance. These are neural crest cells, which will form a variety of diverse structures in later development (see Core Concept 72).

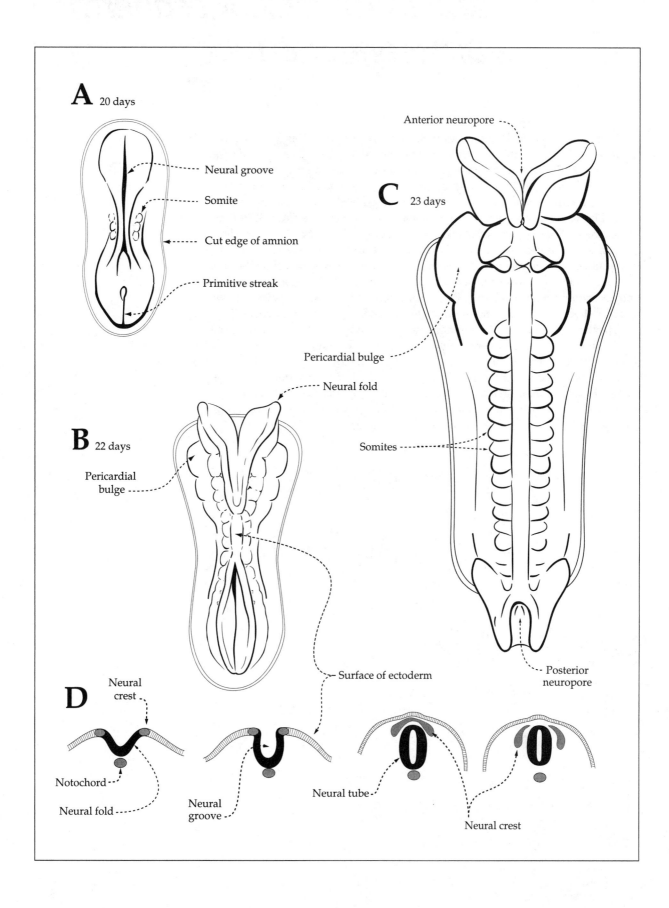

A 20 days

Neural groove
Somite
Cut edge of amnion
Primitive streak

B 22 days

Neural fold
Pericardial bulge
Surface of ectoderm

C 23 days

Anterior neuropore
Pericardial bulge
Somites
Posterior neuropore

D

Neural crest
Notochord
Neural fold
Neural groove
Neural tube
Neural crest

8 / Appearance of Somites and Embryonic Mesoderm Differentiation

Early in the fourth week of development, the intraembryonic mesoderm reorganizes itself. Recall that the cells forming the notochord are already organized as a rodlike cylinder in the embryonic midline. The remaining mesenchymal cells form blocklike epithelial structures along either side of the neural tube. Known as somites, they occur in a regular, repetitive pattern that can be discerned by viewing the embryo from the lateral perspective. ■ **Figs. A and B** ■ Altogether, some 48 pairs of somites develop from a cranial-to-caudal direction, although in the extreme rostral region no obvious somites form. Individual somites are not solid structures but have a cavity, or somitocoele, in their center. Continuous with each somite and extending from them in a ventrolateral direction, the second derivative of the intraembryonic mesoderm develops. ■ **Fig. C** ■ This is the intermediate mesoderm, consisting of a small group of cells that will function in forming a transient embryonic kidney. Finally, lateral and ventral to the intermediate mesoderm, the intracellular mesoderm splits into two layers. See ■ **Fig. C** ■ The layer that becomes associated with the endoderm lining the yolk sac is the visceral or splanchnic mesoderm. The layer associated with surface ectoderm and located dorsolateral to the visceral mesoderm is termed the somatic or parietal layer. In between these two layers of intraembryonic mesoderm, the intraembryonic coelomic cavity will develop.

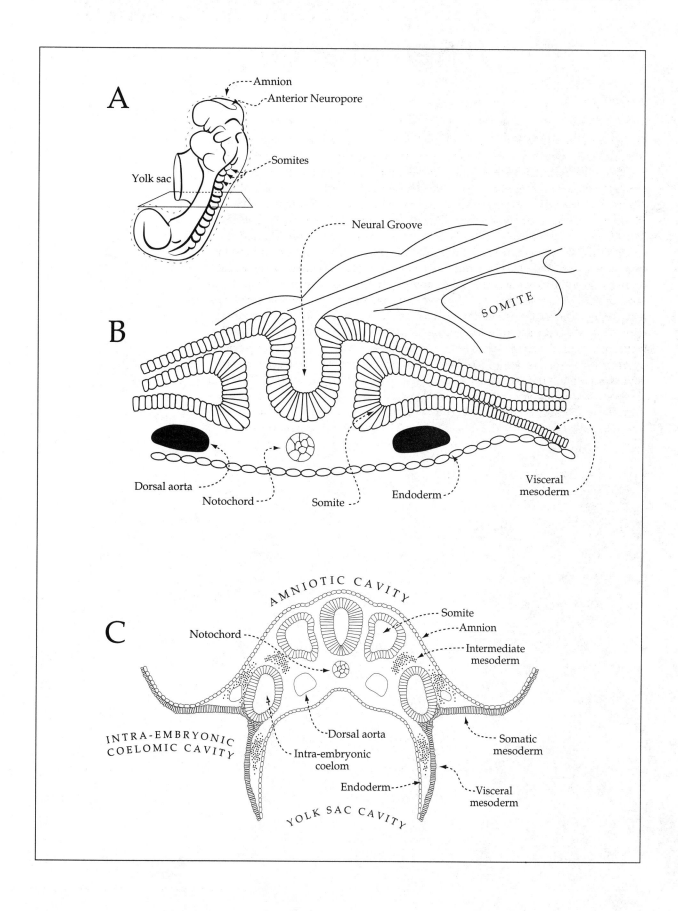

A
Amnion
Anterior Neuropore
Somites
Yolk sac

B
Neural Groove
SOMITE
Dorsal aorta
Notochord
Somite
Endoderm
Visceral mesoderm

C
AMNIOTIC CAVITY
Notochord
Somite
Amnion
Intermediate mesoderm
INTRA-EMBRYONIC COELOMIC CAVITY
Dorsal aorta
Intra-embryonic coelom
Somatic mesoderm
Endoderm
Visceral mesoderm
YOLK SAC CAVITY

9 / *Embryonic Folding*

The transformation of the early disc-shaped embryo into a structure beginning to take on the appearance of a typical embryo occurs largely by the process of embryonic folding. This folding can be thought of as proceeding in two directions. Of course, both occur simultaneously during development.

■ **Figure A** ■ depicts the lateral-to-medial folding in which the lateral plate mesoderm swings ventrally to envelop the proximal portion of the yolk sac. As it does so, the amniotic membrane is also brought ventrally to surround the embryo. The lateral-to-medial folding essentially brings the lateral edges of the embryo together in the midventral line. There these edges fuse in the cranial and caudal regions but leave the middle area, or midgut, still open. Thus the lateral-to-medial folding contributes to the early formation of the gut by pinching off the yolk sac and establishing the intraembryonic coelom.

■ **Figure B** ■ shows the other major folding event, which occurs in the rostral-caudal plane and results in the flexion of the head and tail regions of the embryo toward the midgut. As this folding takes place, structures that were developing in a cranial and caudal position in the trilaminar disc now continue their development in a position ventral to the axis of the embryo. The most notable example is the developing heart in the cranial region and the allantois in the caudal region. The latter structure will eventually be incorporated in the connecting stalk. The appearance of the open midgut is prerequisite for the later development of the umbilical cord.

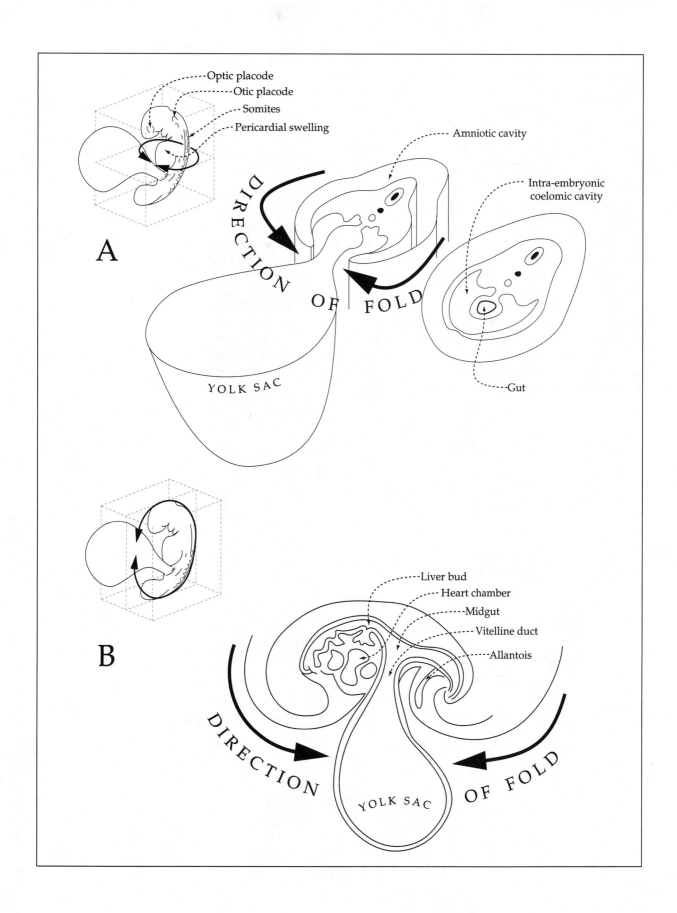

10 / Later Development of the Chorion

As the trophoblast continues to invade the endometrium, the syncytiotrophoblast and the underlying cytotrophoblast begin to form fingerlike projections called villi. At first these villi are nothing more than cytotrophoblast cells surrounded by syncytiotrophoblast. These earliest forms of villi are termed primary villi. Soon the core of the primary villi are invaded by the cells and extracellular matrix of the extraembryonic mesoderm, which comprises the other major component of the chorion. At this stage, villi have a mesenchymal core surrounded by the trophoblast and are termed secondary villi. In their final stage of development, the core of the secondary villi is invaded by embryonic endothelial cells, which form capillaries within the mesenchyme. ■ **Fig. A** ■ The cytotrophoblast thins out to leave the tertiary villi surrounded primarily by syncytiotrophoblast. ■ **Fig. B** ■ These fetal capillaries are ultimately connected by way of the connecting stalk to the developing embryo and soon have blood circulating through them. The tertiary villi are first evident by the end of the third week of development, and over the next month they become more prominent and complex by growth and branching. During this period, the villi exhibit an even distribution around the chorion. Note also that the villi tend to interdigitate between maternal blood spaces, which are in direct contact with the syncytiotrophoblast margin of the villi.

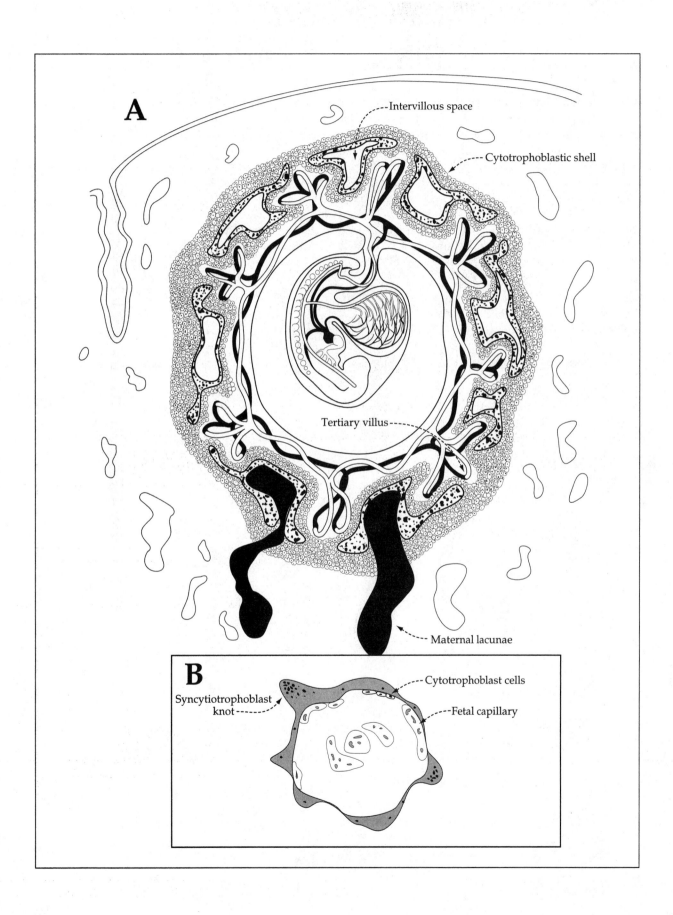

A

Intervillous space

Cytotrophoblastic shell

Tertiary villus

Maternal lacunae

B

Syncytiotrophoblast knot

Cytotrophoblast cells

Fetal capillary

11 / Formation of the Umbilical Cord

As embryonic folding occurs, the broad ventral expanse of the yolk sac becomes dramatically constricted and lined externally by the amnion, which also expands ventrally. ■ **Fig. A** ■ The elongated stalk that remains in continuity with the midgut is the yolk sac stalk or vitelline stalk. The early connecting stalk is derived from the extraembryonic mesoderm and also contains the allantois, the caudal diverticulum off the hindgut region. Within the stalk, prominent blood vessels develop. These will form the paired umbilical arteries and the single umbilical vein. Since the extraembryonic coelom immediately surrounds the vitelline duct, a small potential space exists in the developing umbilical cord. This space becomes important in later development when loops of intestine temporarily occupy this area. ■ **Fig. B** ■

As development proceeds ■ **Fig. C** ■, the umbilical cord becomes longer; it may become knotted, compromising fetal circulation, or it may loop around the embryo itself. The yolk sac stalk becomes extremely attenuated, and the yolk sac itself is often found at the base of the umbilical cord, between the amnion and the chorion. A major component of the mature umbilical cord is the extracellular product of the cord's mesoderm known as Wharton's jelly.

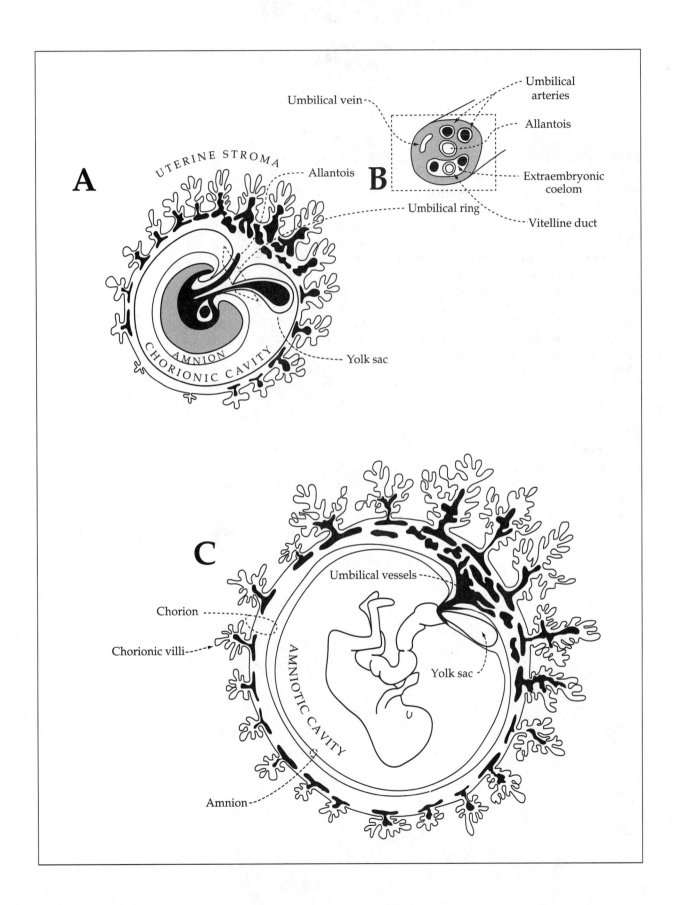

12 / *Final Development of the Chorion and Decidua*

By the second month of development, the chorionic villi are no longer evenly distributed around the chorionic sac. ■ **Fig. A** ■ They become polarized so that they continue to proliferate on the portion of the chorion nearest the developing umbilical cord and thin out and disappear from the rest of the chorion. The part of the chorion in which the villi persist is called the chorion frondosum, or bushy chorion, in contrast to the remaining chorion laeve, or smooth chorion.

Recall that during implantation, the entire blastocyst burrows into the uterine stroma. The implantation site soon heals over, and as the chorion expands into the uterine cavity, three distinct specialized regions of the uterine mucosal lining are observed. The gravid endometrium is generally called the decidua because, like deciduous plants, which lose their leaves every year, it is sloughed off at delivery as the afterbirth. The decidua that overlies the smooth chorion is the decidua capsularis, that portion in proximity to the bushy chorion is the decidua basalis, and the remaining region of the endometrium of pregnancy is the decidua parietalis. See ■ **Fig. A** ■ Note that as the chorion expands to fill up the entire space of the uterine cavity, the amnion fuses with the inner surface of the smooth chorion; as the decidua capsularis thins out due to lack of blood supply, the outer surface of the smooth chorion fuses with the decidua parietalis. ■ **Fig. B** ■

The most important relationship between the chorion and decidua takes place between the chorion frondosum and the decidua basalis. See ■ **Fig. B** ■ These vital structures form the functional placenta.

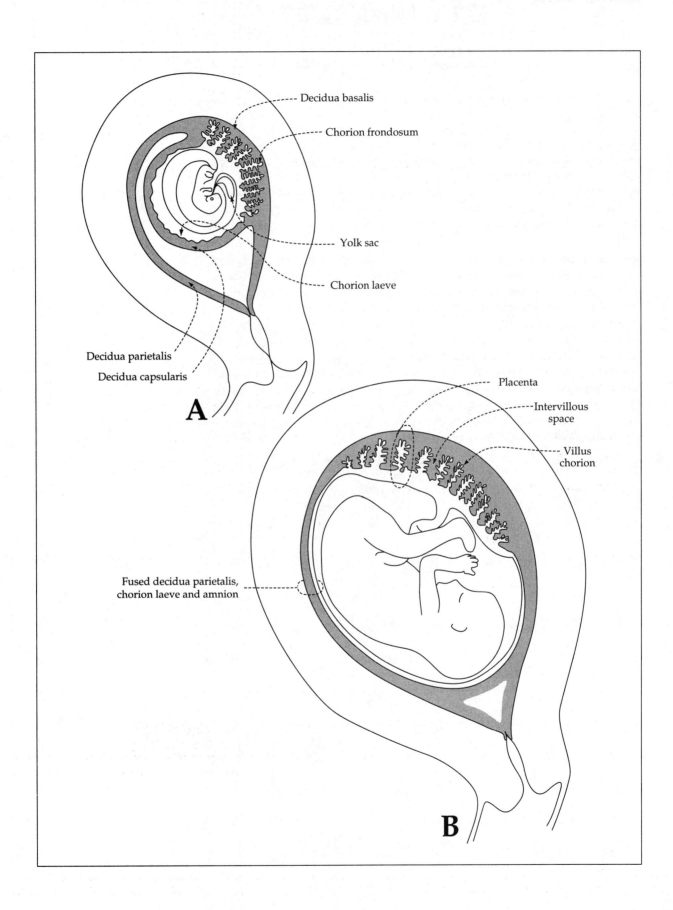

Decidua basalis

Chorion frondosum

Yolk sac

Chorion laeve

Decidua parietalis

Decidua capsularis

A

Placenta

Intervillous space

Villus chorion

Fused decidua parietalis, chorion laeve and amnion

B

13 / Placental Structure and Function

The elaboration of the structural and functional relationship of the chorion frondosum and the decidua basalis culminates in the placenta, which is fully functional in the second trimester. Deoxygenated blood from the fetus is transported by the umbilical arteries, which divide and enter the tertiary villi. ■ **Fig. A** ■ By now these villi have lengthened to such an extent that many originating on the fetal side of the placenta traverse the entire thickness of the placenta to fuse with the decidua basalis. These stem, or anchoring, villi have many lateral tertiary villi branches, termed floating villi. ■ **Fig. B** ■ Maternal blood percolates from maternal spiral arteries in the decidua basalis to the entire intervillous space, formerly the lacunae. On a gross level, connective tissue septa grow inward from the decidua basalis toward the fetal surface of the placenta. These septa divide the placenta into a few dozen compartment-like regions called cotyledons. Viewed from the maternal side, the cotyledons give the placenta a cobblestone-like appearance. Each cotyledon contains two or three anchoring villi.

At the microscopic level, the structural basis for the placental barrier may be observed. ■ **Fig. C** ■ The barrier is entirely fetal, composed of attenuated cells of the syncytiotrophoblast, a small amount of intravillous stroma or connective tissue, and the endothelial lining of the villous capillary. These components are all part of the tertiary villi, which are derived from the chorion. On the maternal side, maternal blood is free in the intervillous spaces. Hence, the human placental barrier is termed hemochorial.

An obvious function of the placenta is to permit gaseous exchange as well as the transfer of nutrients and their waste products. Certain large molecules such as transferrin are nontransferable; however, other substances, including a variety of viruses, can cross the placenta. In addition to its metabolic and transfer role, the placenta is an active endocrine organ, producing chorionic gonadotropin, progesterone, and estrogen.

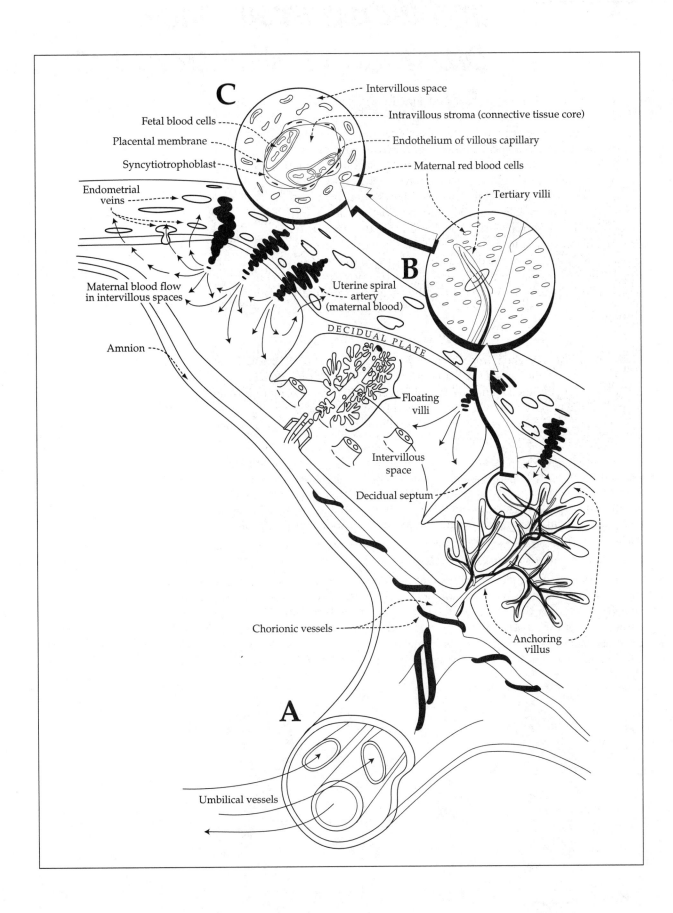

C

Intervillous space

Fetal blood cells

Intravillous stroma (connective tissue core)

Placental membrane

Endothelium of villous capillary

Syncytiotrophoblast

Maternal red blood cells

Endometrial veins

Tertiary villi

B

Maternal blood flow in intervillous spaces

Uterine spiral artery (maternal blood)

DECIDUAL PLATE

Amnion

Floating villi

Intervillous space

Decidual septum

Chorionic vessels

Anchoring villus

A

Umbilical vessels

14 / The Fetal Membranes in Multiple Pregnancy: Dizygotic vs. Monozygotic Twinning

Human twinning is a relatively common event, occurring in more than 1% of live births. A tentative assessment of dizygotic versus monozygotic twinning can sometimes be made based on the basis of the relationship of the chorion and amnion of the two fetuses. This, in turn, is dependent on the relative proximity of the two embryos at the time of implantation. Dizygotic twins implant independently of one another and usually develop completely separate chorions and amnions. As development proceeds, the chorions fill the entire uterine cavity and partially fuse. ■ **Fig. A** ■ Totally separate amnions are maintained throughout pregnancy.

In the case of monozygotic twinning, a range of possible configurations of the fetal membranes exists. This is directly related to the length of time after fertilization when the single developing embryo separates into two embryos. If this time is short, early-division blastomeres may separate from each other with the premature breakdown of the zona pellucida. Independent preimplantation embryos would then reach the endometrium and implant in a manner indistinguishable from that observed with dizygotic twins. See ■ **Fig. A** ■ If the separation takes place later, within the inner cell mass and just before implantation, only one chorion would form with two separate amnions. ■ **Fig. B** ■ If the inner cell masses divide later, they will be very close to one another within the blastocyst. The amnion, which forms shortly after implantation, would envelop both embryos. ■ **Fig. C** ■ Thus, a single chorion with a single or a double amnion would normally arise from monozygotic twinning. In the extreme case where the blastocyst splits partially, conjoint monozygotic twins may arise, sharing various organs.

Monozygotic twinning demonstrates that individual blastomeres can give rise to an entire individual. With development, later blastomeres become progressively restricted in their potency to produce identical embryos. This fundamental fact of embryology has important implications in in vitro fertilization, including such issues as the isolation and culturing of early blastomeres for later implantation and sampling of such cells for genetic characterization.

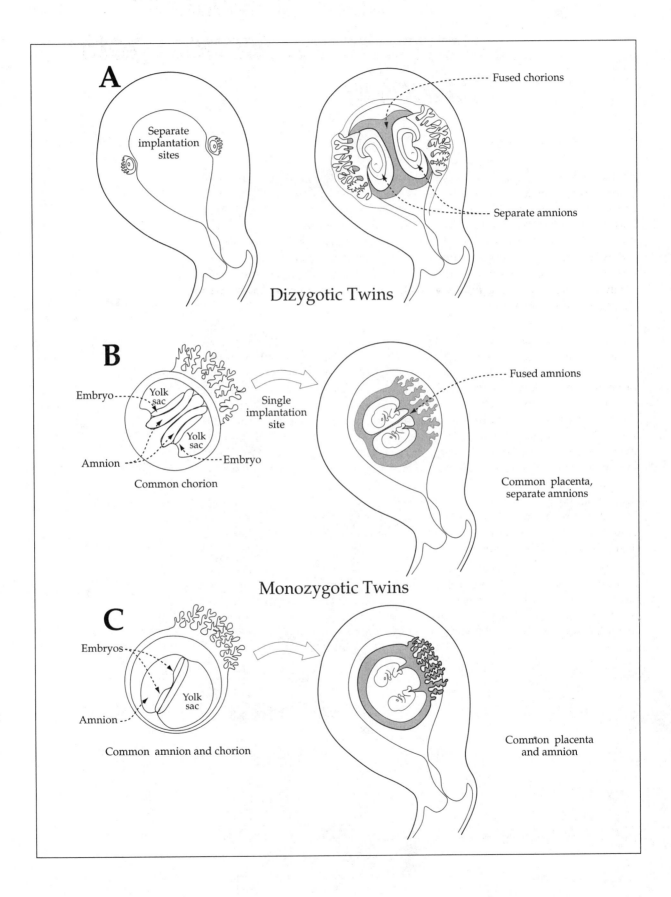

A

Separate implantation sites

Fused chorions

Separate amnions

Dizygotic Twins

B

Embryo

Yolk sac

Amnion

Embryo

Yolk sac

Common chorion

Single implantation site

Fused amnions

Common placenta, separate amnions

Monozygotic Twins

C

Embryos

Amnion

Yolk sac

Common amnion and chorion

Common placenta and amnion

III

Development
of Organ Systems

15 / Somite Differentiation

The first appearance of the somite has been noted earlier (see Core Concept 8). These structures form the basis of not only the skeletal musculature system and the axial skeleton but also the dermis of the skin. The epithelial-like early somite undergoes a major transformation in which some of the cells become mesenchymal and exhibit migratory behavior. The main direction of migration is medial and ventral. ■ **Fig. A** ■ These mesenchymal cells tend to congregate around the notochord and form the precursor of the axial skeleton (see Core Concept 18). This component of the somite is known as the sclerotome. The remainder of the somite remains in a dorsolateral position and differentiates into two other components. The more superficial dermatome forms under the epithelial lining of the embryo and becomes the dermis. The deeper layer differentiates into the myotome and gives rise to most of the skeletal musculature of the trunk and limbs. Before the dermatome and myotome physically separate, they are collectively called the dermomyotome. The segmented dermomyotomes are innervated soon after formation and carry their nerve supply with them as they migrate. The structure undergoes a basic division early in development in which the ventral primary ramus of the spinal nerve innervates the ventral dermomyotomes. This group of developing muscles is collectively named the hypomere, in distinction to the muscles innervated by the dorsal primary ramus, the epimere. ■ **Fig. B** ■ The hypomeric and epimeric components of the body wall later split and contribute to the ventral and dorsal muscle masses, respectively. ■ **Fig. C** ■

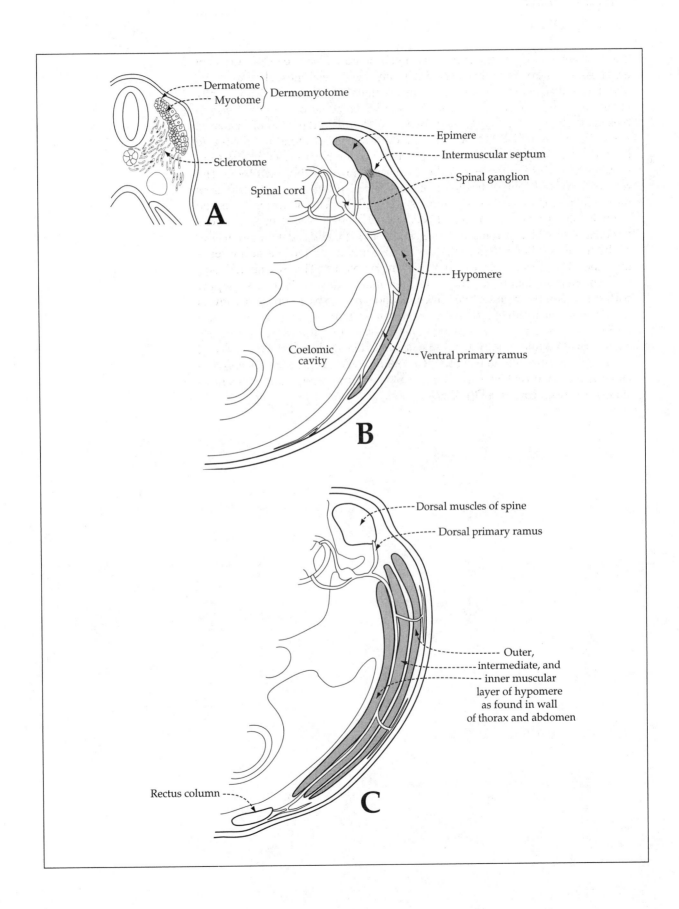

Dermatome ⎱
Myotome ⎰ Dermomyotome

Sclerotome

Epimere

Intermuscular septum

Spinal ganglion

Spinal cord

Hypomere

Coelomic cavity

Ventral primary ramus

A

B

Dorsal muscles of spine

Dorsal primary ramus

Outer, intermediate, and inner muscular layer of hypomere as found in wall of thorax and abdomen

Rectus column

C

16 / Head and Neck Musculature

The regular pattern of paraxial mesoderm in the form of definite somites in the trunk is not as evident in the head and neck region of the early embryo. However, modern morphologic methods have detected a series of slight constrictions in the mesenchyme of this region. These structures are termed somitomeres and are numbered consecutively from the rostral end of the embryo to the most cranial somite. ■ **Fig. A** ■ Seven such somitomeres have been identified, which are in approximate register with the very prominent lateral swellings along the neck of the developing embryo known as pharyngeal or branchial arches. These arches interdigitate with lateral outpouchings of the developing pharynx known as pharyngeal pouches. ■ **Fig. B** ■ Rostral to the first arch are the first three somitomeres, which contribute to the musculature of the extrinsic eye muscles. The first arch coincides with the fourth and fifth somitomeres, the second arch overlaps with somitomere 6, arch 3 with somitomere 7, and the first somite, and the caudal arches (4–6) correspond to the midcervical somites.

The actual cell population that forms the head and neck musculature rostral to the level of the first somite is derived from neural crest cells. These multipotent cells migrate into the area where they differentiate into skeletal muscle. Specific muscles that form this way in the head and neck will be described when considering the muscular derivatives of the pharyngeal arches (see Core Concept 26). Other derivatives of the neural crest cells are discussed in the section on the nervous system (see Core Concept 72).

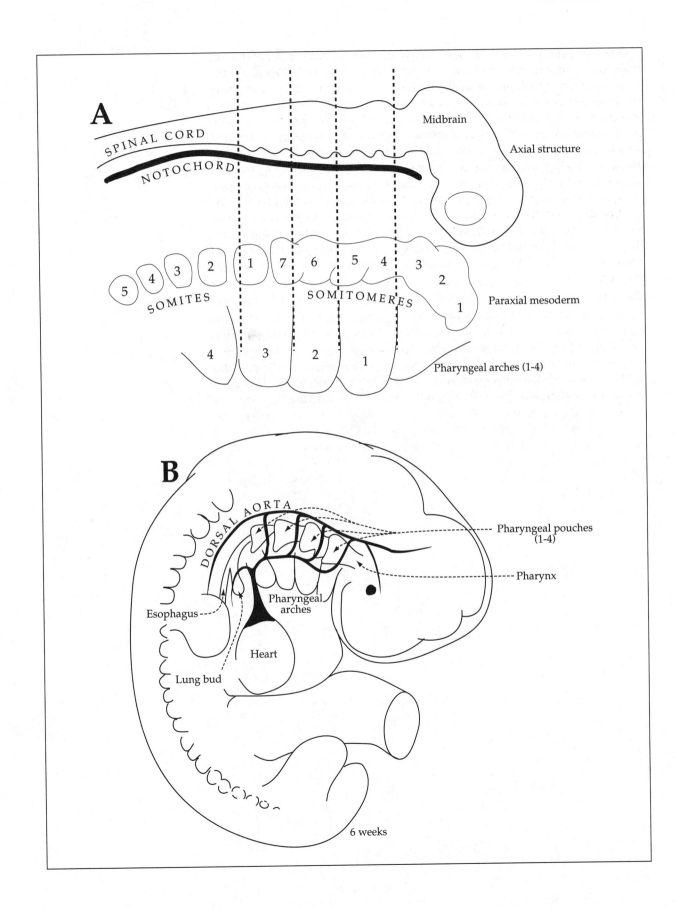

A

SPINAL CORD

NOTOCHORD

Midbrain

Axial structure

5 4 3 2 1 7 6 5 4 3 2 1

SOMITES   SOMITOMERES

Paraxial mesoderm

4 3 2 1

Pharyngeal arches (1-4)

B

DORSAL AORTA

Pharyngeal pouches (1-4)

Pharynx

Pharyngeal arches

Esophagus

Heart

Lung bud

6 weeks

17 / Limb Bud Development

The limbs first appear as outgrowths of the lateral body wall early in the second month of development. These limb buds appear as ectodermal-lined swellings, containing mesenchymal cells capped by an apical ectodermal ridge. These cells arrive from several sources. Myoblastic cells migrate from the myotome portion of the somite, other mesodermal cell populations come from the lateral plate somatopleure, and smaller populations originate from such diverse sources as the neural crest and angioblasts. ■ **Fig. A** ■

Early in their development, sensory and motor neurons grow into the limb buds. These nerves arrive from multiple levels of the spinal cord: those from the more rostral levels (C5, C6, C7) innervate the preaxial, or rostral, portion of the upper limb bud; innervation of the caudal, or postaxial, limb bud is accomplished by more caudal spinal nerves (C8, T1). These initially simple patterns become increasingly more complex as the brachial and lumbosacral plexuses form late in the second month of development when the limb buds rotate around their original axis of reference. The forelimbs rotate laterally and the hind limbs medially, both by 90 degrees. ■ **Fig. B** ■

Concurrent with rotation, condensation of mesenchymal cells into prechondrocytes begins. Precursors of the major long bones appear, as differentiation of the distal limb bud is initiated. ■ **Fig. C** ■ The spatial-temporal regulation of limb bud pattern formation and limb outgrowth is dependent on the presence of the apical ectodermal ridge. Distal limb differentiation proceeds through a series of discreet phases in which the blunt end of the limb bud becomes expanded, or paddle shaped, followed by the thinning out of mesenchyme between the individual digits, resulting in the production of digit rays. The digit rays become notched and then webbed as digit condensation proceeds. Finally, the webbing between digits is eliminated by a process known as programmed cell death, resulting in a morphologically distinguishable hand or foot. ■ **Fig. D** ■

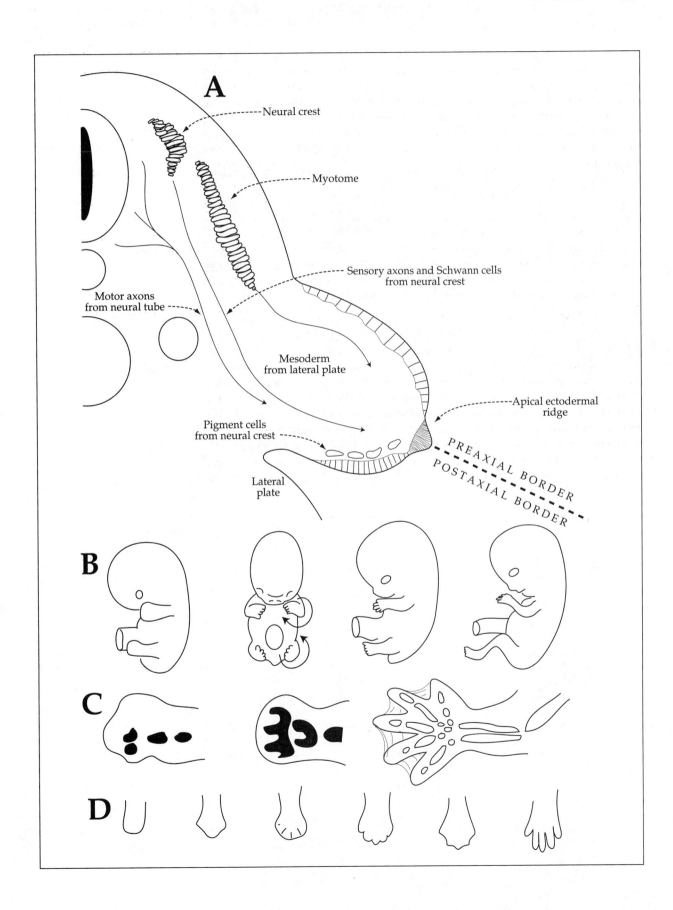

A

Neural crest

Myotome

Sensory axons and Schwann cells from neural crest

Motor axons from neural tube

Mesoderm from lateral plate

Apical ectodermal ridge

Pigment cells from neural crest

PREAXIAL BORDER

POSTAXIAL BORDER

Lateral plate

B

C

D

18 / The Axial Skeleton I: Sclerotome Differentiation

The axial skeleton, comprising the head and the vertebral column, undergoes ossification by several processes. In the vertebrae, the cells of the sclerotome, which are located ventromedially in the somite, migrate medially to surround both the neural canal and the underlying notochord. ■ **Fig. A** ■ Centers of chondrification form around these structures, followed by ossification of the cartilaginous model. ■ **Fig. B** ■ Secondary centers of ossification appear around the former notochord, now greatly expanded to form the center of the body of the vertebra. ■ **Fig. C** ■ This central area of the vertebral body is known as the nucleus pulposus. Other secondary centers form at the distal ends of the vertebral arch. The process of vertebra ossification is initiated in the second month of development and is not completed until well after puberty.

In the thoracic region, cells of the sclerotome will also migrate laterally and ventrally to form the ribs. See ■ **Fig. C** ■ The developing ribs on each side of the embryo migrate toward the ventral midline and fuse with independent mesenchymal condensations, which also develop in the ventral midline and eventually form the sternum.

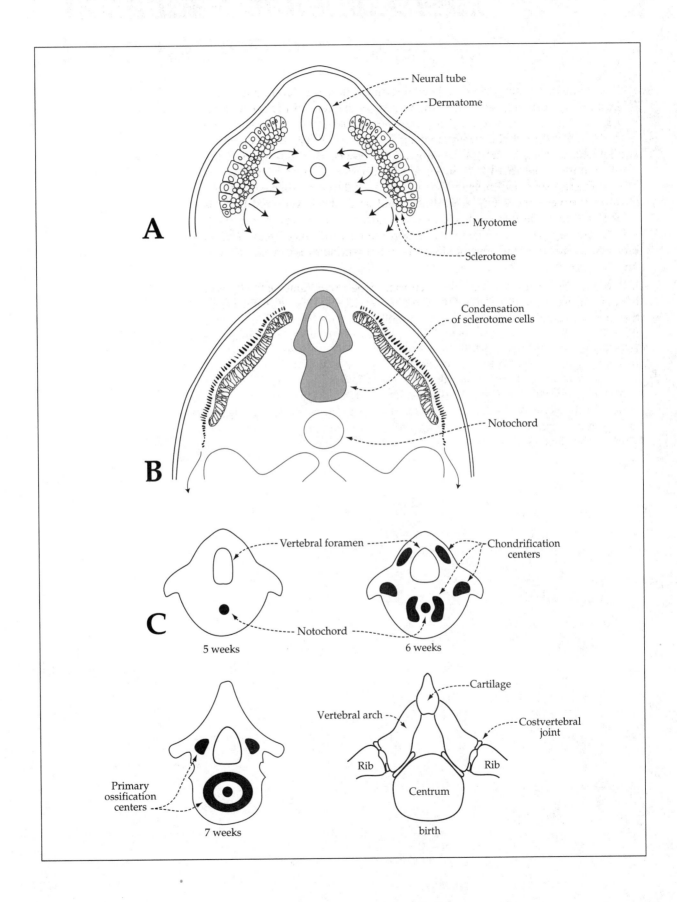

19 / The Axial Skeleton II: The Intersegmental Nature of Vertebrae Development

Although the sclerotome portion of each somite contributes cells that migrate medially to form the vertebrae, their correspondence is not one for one; that is, the sclerotome from one somite does not exclusively form one corresponding vertebrate. This is because each sclerotome splits so that the denser caudal condensation of one sclerotome fuses with the rostral condensation of its neighboring sclerotome.

■ **Figure A** ■ depicts a longitudinal section through the dorsal region of an embryo during vertebrae development. The notochord runs down the midline, and the mesenchyme of the sclerotome migrates toward the midline from the somites. Between each of the somites is found an intersegmental or intervertebral artery from the dorsal aorta. As sclerotome condensation proceeds, ■ **Fig. B** ■, additional mesenchymal condensations appear in the vicinity of the intersegmental arteries. ■ **Fig. C** ■ These will form the anulus fibrosus, or the peripheral part of the sclerotome condensation fusing with the sparsely packed cranial condensation of the adjacent sclerotome. The newly formed vertebrae will straddle two adjacent somites. ■ **Fig. D** ■ At maturity, the intervertebral artery still lies between the somites, which now reside next to the middle of the vertebral body. Note also that the spinal nerves run from the region of the intervertebral disc at the intervertebral foramen, out to the midregion of the somite. ■ **Fig. E** ■

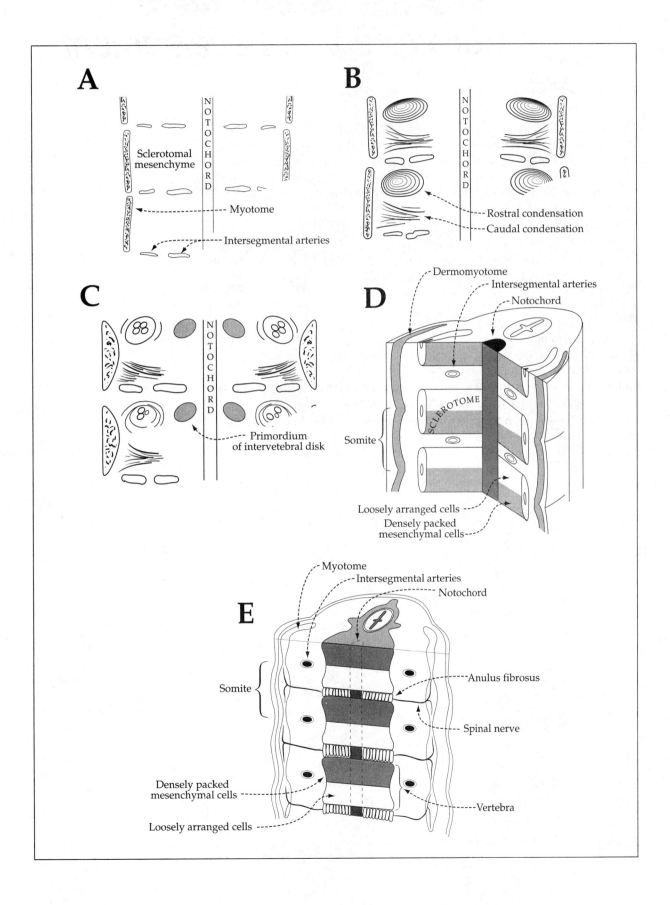

20 / The Axial Skeleton III: Cranial Skeletal Development

The development of the bones of the cranium and jaw is complex. The process may be divided into a consideration of the cranial vault itself, or the neurocranium, and then the jaw and associated structures, or the viscerocranium.

A part of the neurocranium consists of elements of the base of the brain, which form by endochondrial ossification and hence are termed the cartilaginous neurocranium. A parachordal cartilage receives contributions from the sclerotome of the occipital somites, which later ossify around the base of the occipital bone. The ala orbitalis and ala temporalis give rise to the lesser and greater wings of the sphenoid bone, respectively. Periotic cartilages form part of the temporal bone and hypophyseal cartilages, and the trabeculae cranii contribute to the body of the spheroid and ethmoid bones. ■ **Fig. A** ■ The other portion of the neurocranium, which forms the flat bones encasing the brain, is termed the membranous neurocranium. These bones include primarily the paired frontal and parietal bones and the flat, or squamous, portion of the occipital and temporal bones. ■ **Fig. B** ■

The viscerocranium, so named because it is derived from the visceral or branchial arch apparatus, also is composed of elements that form by either endochondrial or intramembranous ossification. The cartilaginous viscerocranium consists of the inner ear bones, the styloid process of the temporal bone, and the hyoid bone. The membranous viscerocranium forms the bulk of this portion of the skull and includes the maxillary bone, a part of the squamous temporal bone, and the mandible. ■ **Fig. C** ■

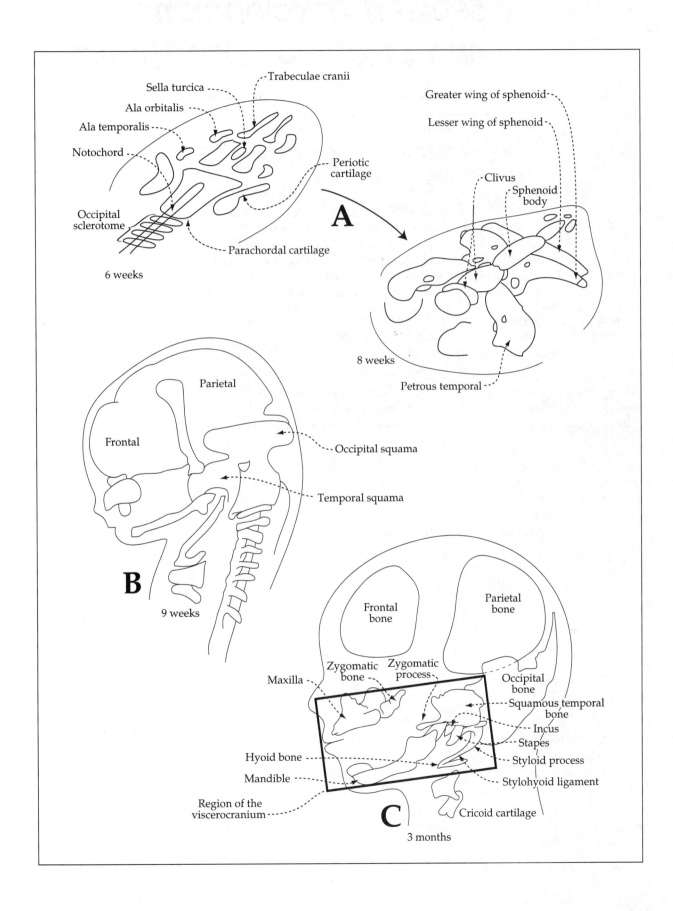

A

Sella turcica
Ala orbitalis
Ala temporalis
Notochord
Trabeculae cranii
Periotic cartilage
Occipital sclerotome
Parachordal cartilage

6 weeks

Greater wing of sphenoid
Lesser wing of sphenoid
Clivus
Sphenoid body
Petrous temporal

8 weeks

B

Parietal
Frontal
Occipital squama
Temporal squama

9 weeks

C

Frontal bone
Parietal bone
Zygomatic bone
Zygomatic process
Maxilla
Occipital bone
Squamous temporal bone
Incus
Stapes
Styloid process
Stylohyoid ligament
Hyoid bone
Mandible
Cricoid cartilage
Region of the viscerocranium

3 months

21 / Development of the Septum Transversum and Diaphragmatic Hernia

The partitioning of the intraembryonic coelomic cavity into a thoracic and abdominal cavity is intimately related to the development of a band of intraembryonic mesoderm that lies just inferior to the developing heart and superior to the liver. This mesoderm is approximately in the transverse plane of the embryo and hence is called the septum transversum. ■ **Fig. A** ■ The septum transversum forms the ventromedial portion of the thoracic-abdominal partition known as the diaphragm. This is the largest component of the diaphragm, known as the central tendon, although it is largely made up of skeletal muscle.

Besides the septum transversum, the diaphragm is composed of three other structures, all of which fuse together. ■ **Fig. B** ■ Laterally and posteriorly, skeletal muscle fibers from the body wall grow inward to form the second component of the diaphragm. In the dorsal midline, the developing esophagus is suspended by its mesentery, which envelops both the aorta and the inferior vena cava. Each of these structures passes through the diaphragm by separate apertures, which originally pierce this third component of the diaphragm, the mesentery of the esophagus. The fourth and final component of the diaphragm are thin, membranous shelves that arise posterior to the septum transversum and lateral to the mesentery of the esophagus. These bilateral structures are the pleuroperitoneal folds.

Failure of the pleuroperitoneal folds to form properly is the most common cause of diaphragmatic herniation. When present, this congenital anomaly occurs almost exclusively on the left side. Although relatively simple to repair postnatally, congenital diaphragmatic hernias have an extremely high mortality rate because the herniation allows abdominal contents to occupy the thoracic cavity and thus interferes with the normal development and maturation of the lung.

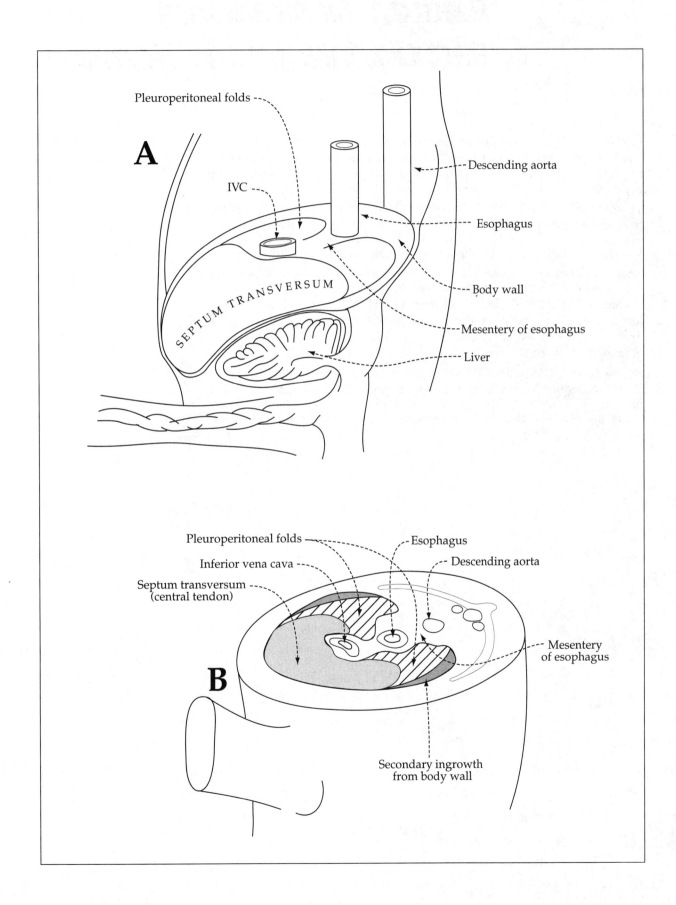

A

Pleuroperitoneal folds

IVC

SEPTUM TRANSVERSUM

Descending aorta

Esophagus

Body wall

Mesentery of esophagus

Liver

B

Pleuroperitoneal folds

Inferior vena cava

Septum transversum
(central tendon)

Esophagus

Descending aorta

Mesentery
of esophagus

Secondary ingrowth
from body wall

22 / Development of the Pleuropericardial Partitioning

Concurrent with the partitioning of the intracoelomic cavity into an abdominal and thoracic compartment, by the development of the diaphragm the thoracic cavity itself is further subdivided into a pleural and pericardial compartment by the pleuropericardial membrane.

The pleuropericardial membrane begins as bilateral folds of tissue lined with coelomic mesoderm that grow medially toward each other at a level between the ventrally lying heart and the dorsal foregut. Within these folds are two important structures: the phrenic nerve, which innervates the diaphragm, and the common cardinal vein, which contributes to the formation of the superior vena cava. ■ **Figs. A and B** ■ As the pleuropericardial folds fuse in the midline separating the developing heart and foregut, lung buds grow laterally out of the foregut (see Core Concept 47) into the newly forming pleural cavity. ■ **Fig. C** ■ As the lung buds continue to grow ventrally, the.pleural cavity precedes it until it approaches the ventrolateral body wall. ■ **Fig. D** ■

By this series of developmental events, the pleuropericardial membranes are largely transformed into the fibrous pericardium in which the phrenic nerves run. Lateral to the fibrous pericardium lies the potential space of the pleural cavity, lined with parietal and visceral pleura.

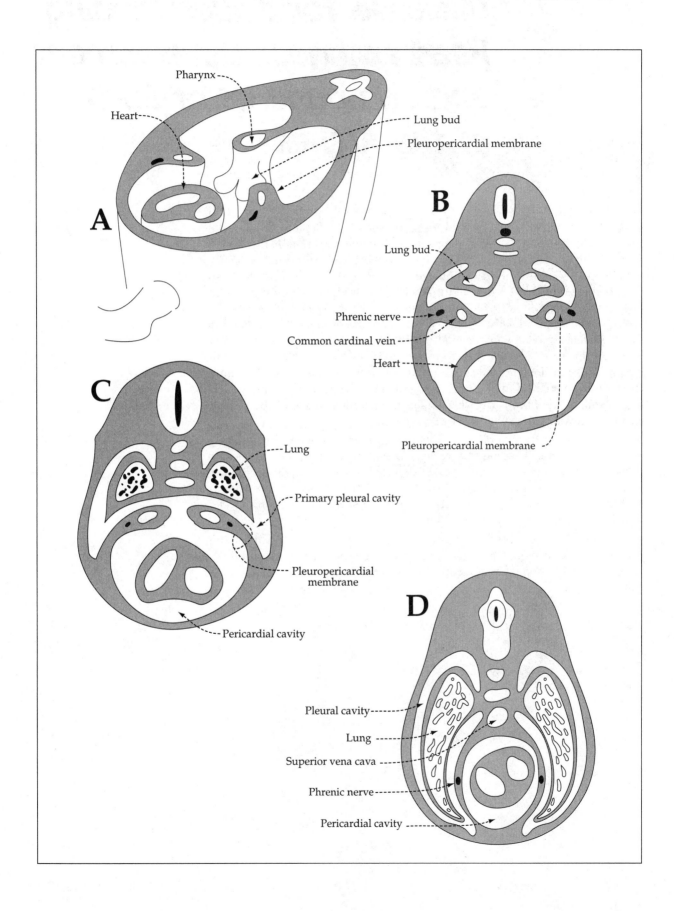

A
Pharynx
Heart
Lung bud
Pleuropericardial membrane

B
Lung bud
Phrenic nerve
Common cardinal vein
Heart
Pleuropericardial membrane

C
Lung
Primary pleural cavity
Pleuropericardial membrane
Pericardial cavity

D
Pleural cavity
Lung
Superior vena cava
Phrenic nerve
Pericardial cavity

23 / The Branchial Apparatus as the Basis for Understanding Head and Neck Development and Components of Each of the Arches

The anatomic basis of head and neck development centers around the branchial apparatus. This series of repeating structures is evolutionarily related to the gill system of lower vertebrates, hence the name **branchial.** Because these arches primarily reside along the developing pharynx, they are also termed the pharyngeal arches. ■ **Fig. A** ■ Each of these arches projects medially into the ventral portion of the oropharynx and consequently interdigitates with pouches or lateral extensions of the primitive oropharynx. ■ **Fig. B** ■ These pouches project so far laterally that they approach the groove or cleft between the external arches to form structures called the branchial membranes. This positioning can best be appreciated by viewing the embryo in a frontal section. ■ **Fig. C** ■

Each of the four components of the branchial apparatus — the arch, pouch, cleft, and membrane — gives rise to specific embryologic derivatives involved in head and neck development. In addition, each arch contains four components key to understanding this region. These are arch-associated specific nerves, cartilages, muscles, and arteries, depicted schematically in ■ **Fig. C** ■ in which the dorsal half of the embryo is viewed from the ventral aspect. In ■ **Fig. B** ■, the arteries of the branchial arches are seen coursing through the individual arches between the pouches.

An understanding of these basic concepts is prerequisite to understanding head and neck development. Each component of the branchial arch system, as well as each component of the entire branchial apparatus, will be systematically followed.

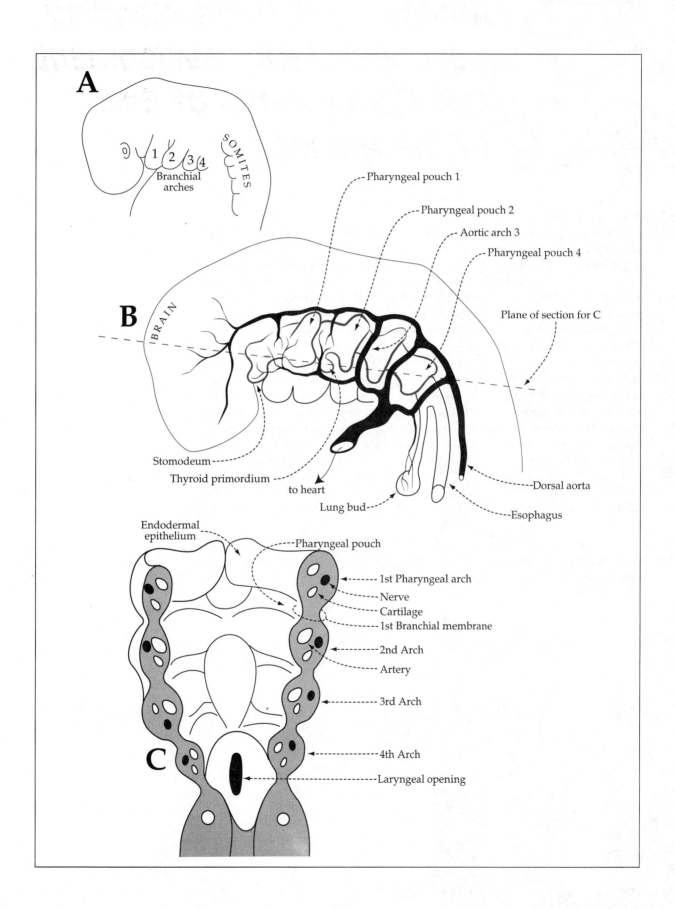

24 / Nerves of the Branchial Arches

The branchial arches by convention are often identified by Roman numerals. This is obvious for the first three arches: I, II, and III. However, the fourth arch presents a complication. This last arch may be considered a fusion of the fourth and sixth branchial arches and is called either arch IV or arch IV–VI. In humans the fifth is rudimentary and does not give rise to specific structures.

Each of the arches is associated with a specific cranial nerve that grows inferiorly from the brain into its arch and provides the innervation to all the future derivatives of that arch. Because these nerves supply the branchial arches, they are referred to as branchial nerves. ■ **Fig. A** ■ In the first arch, innervation is by the massive trigeminal nerve (cranial nerve V). Its most inferior division, the mandibular division (V3), actually grows into the main portion of arch I; hence it is also called the mandibular arch. The more superior maxillary division (V2) will innervate the superior subdivision of arch I, known as the maxillary process. The most rostral division of cranial nerve V, the ophthalmic division (V1), provides primarily sensory innervation to rostal structures in the developing head and facial region.

The second branchial arch is innervated by the facial nerve (cranial nerve VII). The third arch, which is the smallest, is associated with the glossopharyngeal nerve (cranial nerve IX). Finally, the fourth arch is supplied by the vagus nerve (cranial nerve X). Since this is a "fused" arch, its innervation may be subdivided into two specific branches of the vagus: superiorly the superior laryngeal nerve (the nerve of arch IV), and inferiorly the recurrent laryngeal nerve (the nerve of arch VI) ■ **Fig. B** ■

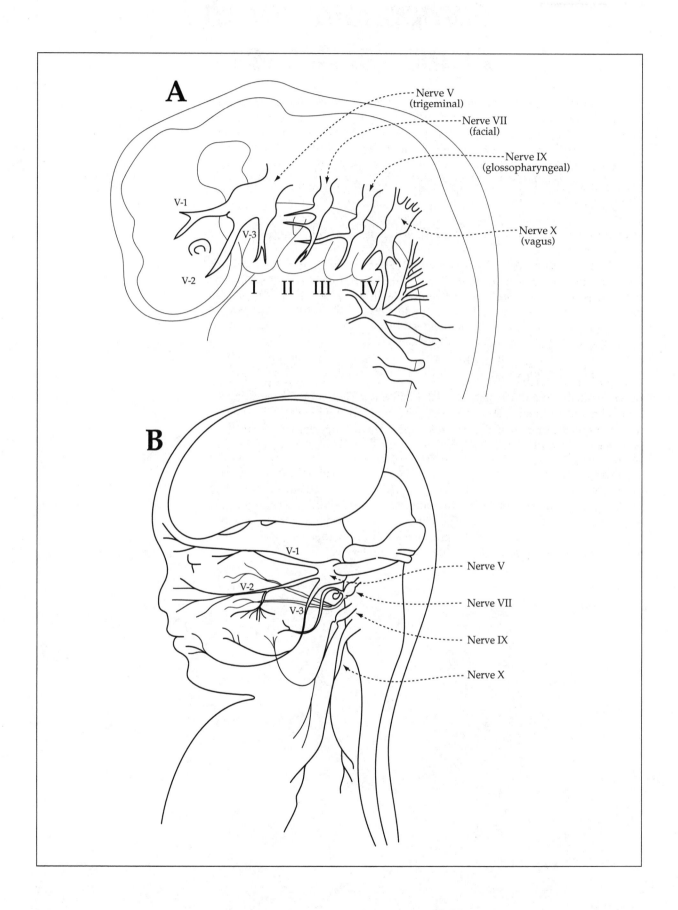

A

Nerve V
(trigeminal)

Nerve VII
(facial)

Nerve IX
(glossopharyngeal)

Nerve X
(vagus)

V-1

V-3

V-2

I   II   III   IV

B

V-1

V-2

V-3

Nerve V

Nerve VII

Nerve IX

Nerve X

25 / Cartilage and Skeletal Components of the Branchial Arches

The mesenchymal cells, which reside in the branchial arches and give them their characteristic bulging appearance, arrive at this position by migrating from the dorsal midbrain and hindbrain region. ■ **Fig. A** ■ These are pleuripotent neural crest cells (see Core Concept 72), which in the branchial arches give rise to both the cartilaginous elements as well as the mesenchyme, which later ossifies by intramembranous chondification to form the mandible, parts of the maxilla and palate, and a host of other structures in the head. ■ **Fig. B** ■

Each branchial arch contains a cartilaginous element, which may either largely regress during development or survive to differentiate into an ossified or a cartilaginous structure. ■ **Fig. C** ■ The first arch cartilage is mostly represented by the large Meckel's cartilage located in the position of the future lower jaw, or mandible. The other part of the first arch cartilage is the future malleus and incus bones of the inner ear. Meckel's cartilage itself regresses to leave the insignificant sphenomandibular ligament, and the mesenchyme around this area subsequently develops into the mandible by intramembranous ossification.

The second arch cartilage, also relatively large in the early embryo, is sometimes referred to as Reichert's cartilage. Elements of this cartilage later ossify to produce the remaining ear ossicle, the stapes, the styoid process of the temporal bone of the skull, and a portion of the hyoid bone, its lesser horn. In addition, a small ligament between the styoid process and the hyoid bone, the stylohyoid ligament, is derived from the second branchial arch cartilage. The third arch cartilage, a much smaller structure, forms the precursor of the rest of the hyoid bone, its greater horn. The fourth arch cartilage gives rise to the cartilaginous elements of the larynx. These include not only the major cartilages — the thyroid and cricoid — but also the smaller but nonetheless important arytenoids and other minor cartilages intrinsic to the larynx.

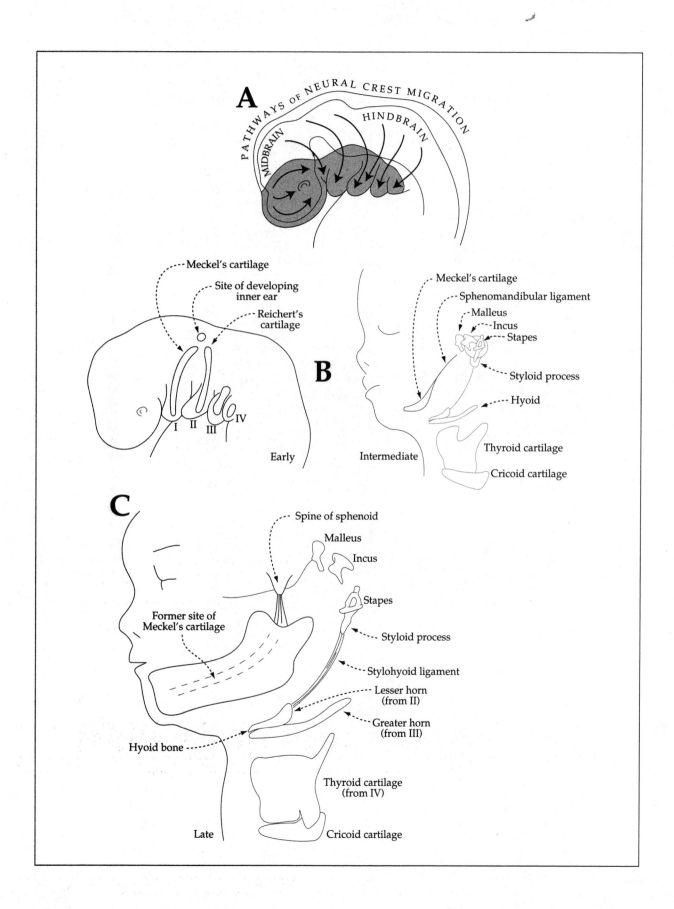

26 / Muscles of the Branchial Arches

The skeletal muscle of the head and neck region is formed from myogenic precursor cells that migrate into the branchial arches from the caudal group of somitomeres and the most rostral somites. These cells differentiate into a wide variety of individual muscles, which are best learned by studying them as functionally related embryologic groups. ■ **Fig. A** ■

Derivatives of the branchial arch muscular components are shown in ■ **Fig. B** ■. The first arch musculature, as in the case of first arch nerves and cartilaginous-skeletal derivatives, forms the most prominent group of structures. These include the powerful muscles of mastication: the temporalis, masseter, and medial and lateral pterygoid muscles. In addition, the first arch gives rise to two tensors — one of the palate, the tensor veli palatini; the other of the auditory tube, the tensor tympani — and two muscles in the floor of the mouth — the anterior digastric and the mylohyoid.

The second arch contributes to a large number of muscles collectively known as the muscles of facial expression. These very thin muscles originate and insert in the skin, are found throughout the face and neck, and are exemplified by such diverse individual members as the frontalis, orbicularis oris and oculi, zygomaticus, and platysma. The remaining second arch muscles are the small stapedius of the inner ear, the stylohyoid, and the posterior belly of the digastric.

The third arch contributes to only one muscle, the stylopharyngeus, while the fourth arch forms muscles of the pharynx and larynx, including the pharyngeal constrictors. The cricothyroid muscle is derived from branchial arch IV, whereas all the remaining intrinsic laryngeal musculature is from arch VI.

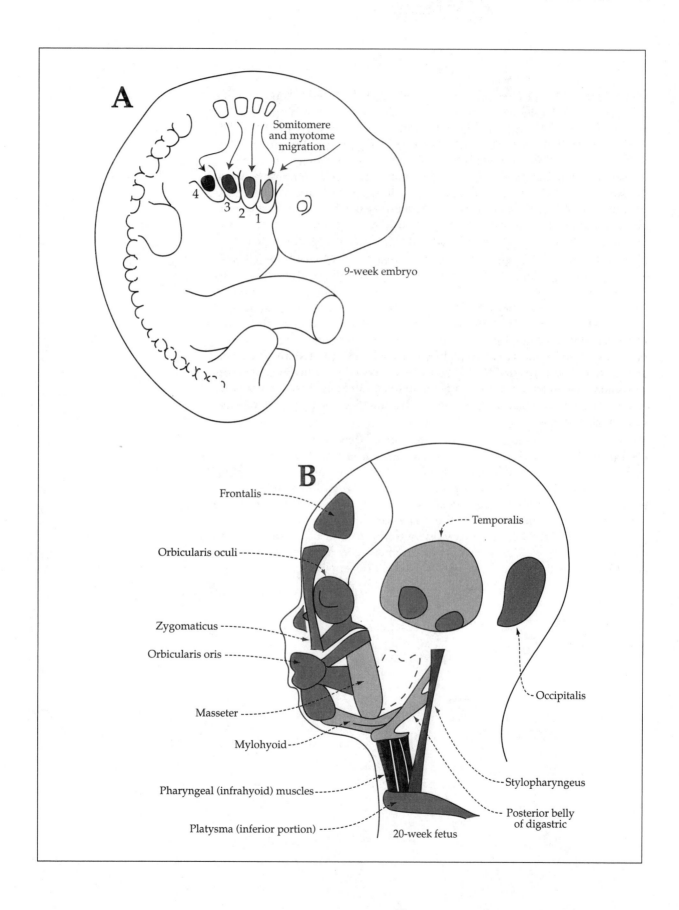

A

Somitomere and myotome migration

4 3 2 1

9-week embryo

B

Frontalis

Temporalis

Orbicularis oculi

Zygomaticus

Orbicularis oris

Masseter

Mylohyoid

Occipitalis

Pharyngeal (infrahyoid) muscles

Stylopharyngeus

Platysma (inferior portion)

Posterior belly of digastric

20-week fetus

27 / Arteries of the Branchial Arches

Unlike in the case of the branchial nerves, cartilages, and muscles in which the first two arches predominate, the development of the branchial arch arteries, commonly called the aortic arches, follows the opposite pattern. ■ **Fig. A** ■ The first aortic arch becomes relatively small to give rise to a portion of the maxillary and possibly the external carotid arteries. The second arch also largely regresses after the first month of development, but the remainder develops into the small hyoid and stapedial arteries. As with the other branchial arch components, the fifth aortic arch is transitory and does not contribute to any adult structures.

Thus, the important aortic arches are the third, fourth, and sixth arches. The third aortic arch forms part of the carotid system. This includes both the common carotids and a short proximal portion of the internal carotid arteries. The fourth and sixth arches are asymmetric, giving rise to different adult structures on each side of the embryo. The fourth arch gives rise to a small segment of the arch of the aorta on the left side. On the right side, the fourth arch forms a proximal portion of the right subclavian artery, which at this stage is continuous with the seventh intersegmental artery. In a schematic fashion, the aortic arch system is shown in ■ **Fig. B** ■. Only specific portions of the original arches are retained; the majority of this arterial system is obliterated. (Additional information on the aortic arches is presented in the next section on cardiovascular development.)

The sixth aortic arch forms quite distinctly from the others. Looking at the embryo from the ventral side with the heart removed ■ **Fig. C** ■, it forms as a plexus of arteries growing in medially from the dorsal aortae around the pharynx and lung buds (see Core Concept 47), which then coalesce and join with either the fourth arch or more caudally with the dorsal aortae. These are the left and right pulmonary arteries. The pulmonary artery on the right side regresses, whereas the left pulmonary artery forms a more proximal (closer to the heart) portion of the adult pulmonary artery and a more distal arterial shunt known as the ductus arteriosus (see Core Concept 41).

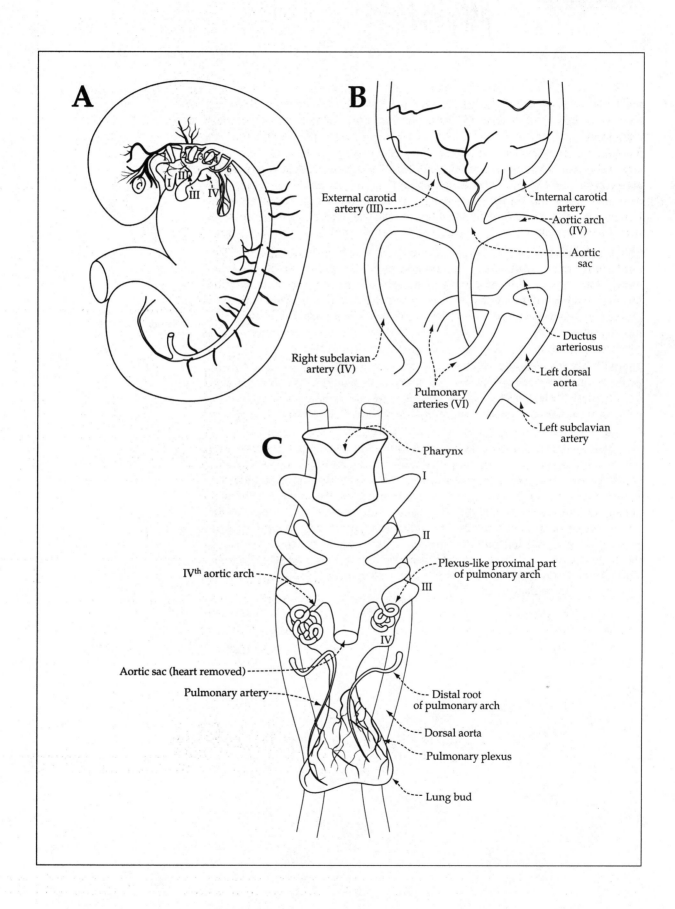

A

B

External carotid artery (III)

Internal carotid artery

Aortic arch (IV)

Aortic sac

Ductus arteriosus

Right subclavian artery (IV)

Left dorsal aorta

Pulmonary arteries (VI)

Left subclavian artery

C

Pharynx

I

II

IVth aortic arch

Plexus-like proximal part of pulmonary arch

III

IV

Aortic sac (heart removed)

Pulmonary artery

Distal root of pulmonary arch

Dorsal aorta

Pulmonary plexus

Lung bud

28 / Derivatives of the Branchial Pouches

Interdigitating with the branchial arches are the lateral extensions of the pharynx known as the branchial pouches. Like the arches, there are four branchial pouches, each located along the inferior border of its respectively named arch. ■ **Fig. A** ■

The first pouch extends the most laterally to form the tubotympanic recess, which forms around the ear ossicles. ■ **Fig. B** ■ This recess will develop into the tympanic cavity, which will become elongated to form the auditory tube. The second pouch is very shallow and accumulates lymphoid tissue around itself. This aggregation of lymphatics will develop into the palatine tonsil, whereas the remnant of the pouch itself is known as the supratonsillar fossa.

The third and fourth branchial pouches have more complicated fates. The third pouch differentiates into the inferior parathyroid gland from its more superior portion and the thymus gland from its more inferior portion. Similarly, the fourth pouch develops into two separate structures. Its superior part forms the superior parathyroid, while the inferior part contributes to the ultimobranchial (postbranchial) body.

Although it is not strictly a branchial pouch derivative, the thyroid gland begins its development as a ventral midline diverticulum at the level of the first branchial pouch. See ■ **Fig. B** ■ As this diverticulum continues to grow ventrally and caudally, it is termed the thyroglossal duct. If development proceeds normally, the thyroglossal duct completes its migration in the vicinity of the thyroid and cricoid cartilages and becomes obliterated as the thyroid gland develops in this position. The thymus, parathyroid glands, and ultimobranchial bodies also migrate inferiorly. The thymus attains its final position just inferior to the thyroid gland. Near the thymus's superior pole, the parathyroid gland from the third pouch (parathyroid III) reaches a position close to the inferior pole of the thyroid gland and hence is termed the inferior parathyroid. In contrast, the parathyroid from the fourth pouch (parathyroid IV) migrates to the superior pole of the thyroid and becomes the superior parathyroid. The ultimobranchial bodies usually end up in the thyroid gland inferior to parathyroid IV and superior to parathyroid III.

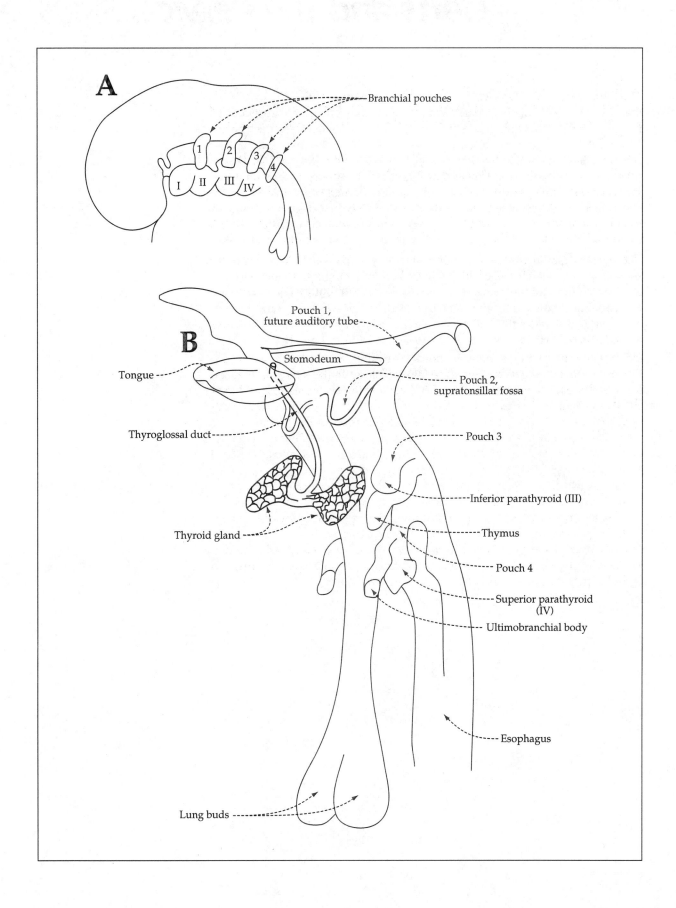

29 / The Fate of the Branchial Clefts and the Cervical Sinus

The branchial clefts or grooves are the structures between the branchial arches that give the neck of the 6-week embryo its characteristically furrowed appearance. ■ **Fig. A** ■ Only the first of these clefts, residing between the first and second arch, will give rise to an adult structure. This is the external auditory meatus, which meets the first branchial pouch to form the first branchial membrane, or the tympanic membrane. The tympanic membrane consists of an ectodermal outer lining from the first cleft and endodermal inner lining from the first pouch. As development proceeds, a series of six hillocks, or ridges, form around the external auditory meatus and later differentiate into the external ear. ■ **Fig. B** ■

The remaining branchial clefts are obliterated by an inferior overgrowth of the second and third arch mesenchyme, best seen by taking a coronal section of the embryo through the plane depicted in ■ **Fig. A** ■. ■ **Figure C** ■ shows such a section, illustrating only the right half of this region. As this envelopment takes place, a sinus or fluid-filled space transiently remains behind. This cervical sinus is the remnant of the second, third, and fourth branchial clefts. As a result of this process, the contour of the neck is smoothed out. Occasionally the cervical sinus persists and may retain its embryologic connection to the pharynx (branchial sinus) or to both the pharynx and the outside of the neck (branchial fistula).

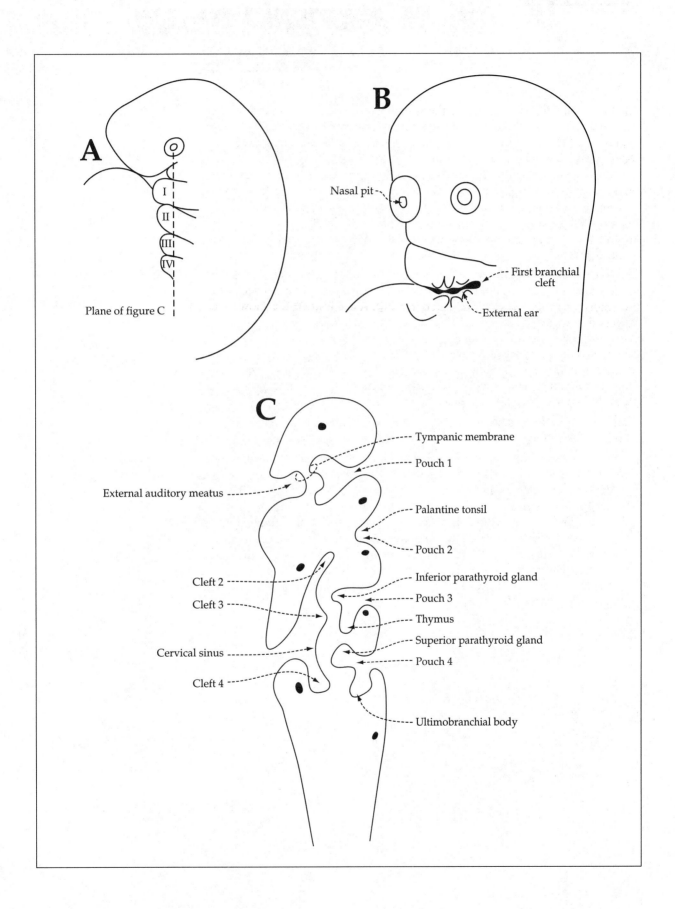

A

I

II

III

IV

Plane of figure C

B

Nasal pit

First branchial cleft

External ear

C

Tympanic membrane

Pouch 1

External auditory meatus

Palantine tonsil

Pouch 2

Cleft 2

Inferior parathyroid gland

Cleft 3

Pouch 3

Thymus

Cervical sinus

Superior parathyroid gland

Pouch 4

Cleft 4

Ultimobranchial body

30 / Development of the Tongue in Relationship to the Branchial Pouches

The floor of the pharynx early in the second month of development contains shallow furrows, which represent the position of the branchial pouches. These furrows extend medially in the floor of the pharynx and become interrupted by two tandem midline swellings. The anterior swelling is the tuberculum impar or median tongue bud. This structure is part of the first branchial arch. Immediately posterior to the tuberculum impar is a larger midline swelling known as the copula, which straddles the second, third, and fourth arches. ■ **Fig. A** ■

The body of the tongue develops as the floor of the first arch mesenchyme greatly expands. These paired lateral lingual swellings grow anteriorly and fuse in the midline with each other and the tuberculum impar. ■ **Fig. B** ■ The tuberculum impar is demarcated from the copula by a pit called the foramen cecum. It is this foramen through which the thyroglossal duct descends (see Core Concept 28). The posterior third of the tongue develops by the anterior overgrowth of the third arch mesenchyme to cover the second arch. This results in the characteristic V-shaped border at the junction of the body and posterior tongue. Finally, at the level of the fourth arch, another midline mesenchymal proliferation, the epiglottal swelling, and its associated lateral expansions, the arytenoid swellings, begin to form around the glottis. ■ **Fig. C** ■

Because it forms from portions related to all four branchial arches, the innervation of the tongue is complex. The first arch nerve (trigeminal) conveys general sensation, whereas the second arch nerve (facial) carries special sensation (taste) to the body of the tongue. Taste to the posterior tongue is mediated by the third arch nerve (glossopharyngeal). The epiglottis, arytenoids, and extreme posterior part of the tongue are innervated by the fourth arch nerve (vagus) by its superior laryngeal branch. The motor innervation to the entire tongue, as well as to its extrinsic musculature, is by way of the hypoglossal nerve. Thus, portions of five cranial nerves (V, VII, IX, X, and XII) contribute to supply the tongue.

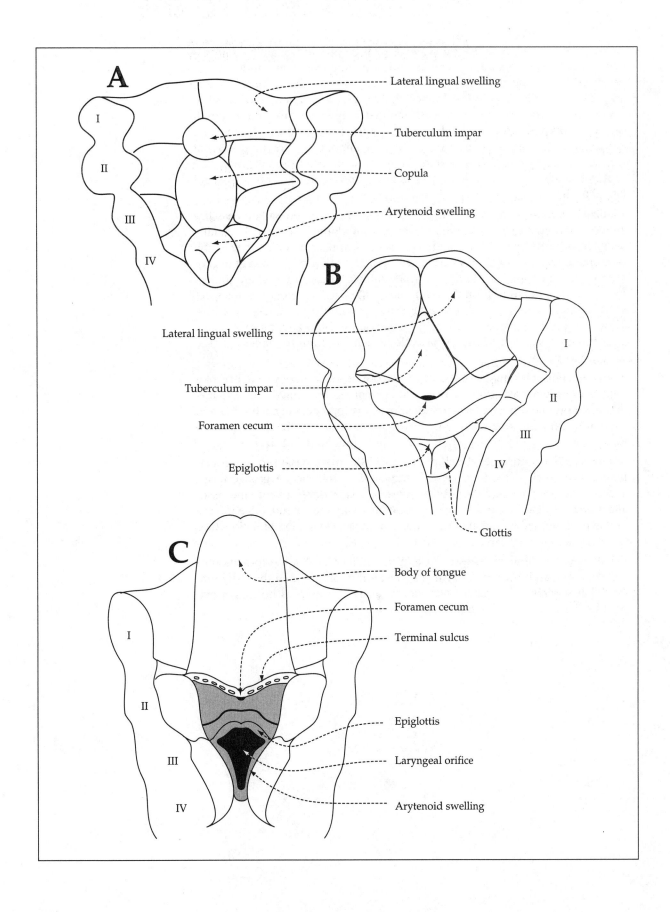

31 / *Facial Development*

Facial development centers around the expansion and movement of the two major structures evident at the cranial end of the embryo by the fourth week postfertilization. The more rostral of the structures is the frontonasal process, and inferiolaterally lies the first branchial arch. Viewing the embryo from the ventral aspect, the frontonasal process and first arch encircle the future mouth of the embryo, a structure known as the stomodeum. Very early, the first branchial arch gives rise to two separate components: the more caudal mandibular process, which is located below the stomodeum, and the maxillary process, which resides between the mandibular and frontonasal processes and lateral to the stomodeum. ■ **Fig. A** ■

As development proceeds, the mesenchyme of the frontonasal process expands and migrates toward the midventral line. Simultaneously, bilaterally symmetrical ectodermal thickenings, or placodes, appear on either side of the frontonasal process. ■ **Fig. B** ■ These nasal placodes become relatively thicker around their periphery and thin out in the middle to the point where the ectoderm breaks down to form the nasal pit. ■ **Fig. C** ■ Two other placodes develop farther laterally and also migrate ventrally with the frontonasal process. These are the lens placode, where the eye will develop, and, more caudally and dorsally, the otic or auditory placode, which will form the inner ear (see Core Concepts 74 and 75).

The peripheral thickenings of the nasal placode result in the appearance of a medial and lateral nasal prominence. As they approach each other, the two medial nasal prominences form the external nose by approaching each other and eventually fusing midventrally. Just below the nose in the midline, the frontonasal process also forms the philtrum of the upper lip. ■ **Fig. D** ■

As the maxillary processes develop, they meet the frontonasal process at two points. The first is at the juncture with the nasal prominence. A groove forms at this position, sinks into the mesenchyme, and later develops into the nasolacrimal duct. The second is at the juncture with the lateral edge of the philtrum. This region is "smoothed out" by mesenchyme proliferation (see Core Concept 32).

Finally, the mandibular processes fuse in the midline during the formation of the mandible and lower lip. ■ **Fig. E** ■ The furrow observed in the early embryo that separates the mandibular and maxillary processes is no longer evident by the end of the first trimester.

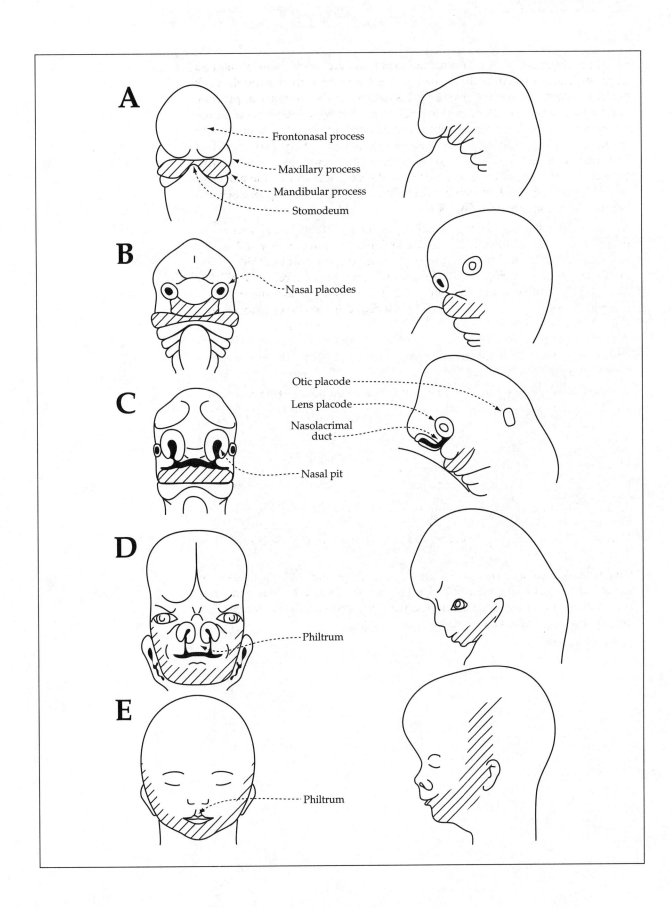

A — Frontonasal process — Maxillary process — Mandibular process — Stomodeum

B — Nasal placodes

C — Otic placode — Lens placode — Nasolacrimal duct — Nasal pit

D — Philtrum

E — Philtrum

32 / Primary and Secondary Palate Development and Etiology of Cleft Palate and Lip

The palate is embryologically formed from two separate components that subsequently fuse together. The first component is the primary palate. This is a part of the frontonasal process (described in Core Concept 31), which not only forms the midface and philtrum but also continues internally to form the intermaxillary segment or median palatine process. The primary palate lies between the oral cavity (former stomodeum) and the nasal pit. In parasagittal section, as the nasal cavity expands dorsally, the oronasal membrane between the nasal and oral cavities thins out and finally breaks down to permit continuity between the nasal and oropharynx. ■ **Fig. A** ■

Viewed from below, the primary palate, located in the ventral midline, makes contact with the bilaterally paired lateral palatine shelves ■ **Fig. B** ■ as they swing from a vertical to a horizontal position, as seen in a frontal view. ■ **Fig. C** ■ The shelves grow toward the midline and fuse with the primary palate, as well as with one another, to form the secondary palate. Concomitantly, the nasal septum grows inferiorly in the midline to fuse with the secondary palate along its seam. See ■ **Fig. C** ■ After ossification, the primary palate contains the four incisor teeth and the incisive foramen. It is referred to as the premaxillary portion of the maxilla.

The etiology of the common form of cleft lip may be understood from normal facial development discussed in Core Concept 31. The lateral edge of the philtrum, derived from the frontonasal process, fails to fuse fully with the medial edge of the maxillary process. ■ **Fig. D** ■ This may occur unilaterally, as depicted, or bilaterally. In cleft palate, either one or both of the secondary palatal shelves fail to meet in the midline. ■ **Fig. E** ■ Clefting of the primary palate in which the median palatine process does not fuse with the secondary palate can also occur. ■ **Fig. F** ■ Although cleft lip and cleft palate are separate congenital malformations, they are often associated with one another, as exemplified in ■ **Fig. G** ■, where a unilateral cleft occurs in the lip, primary palate, and secondary palate.

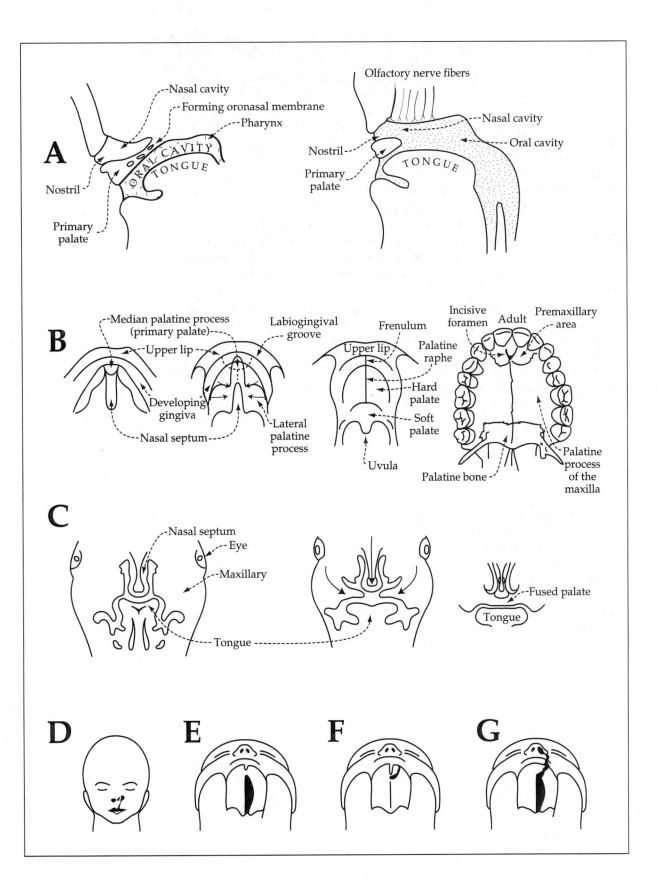

33 / Development of Dentition

The development of the teeth is an excellent example of an important general mechanism in embryology: the interaction of epithelium and its underlying mesenchyme to produce specific, differentiated structures. In the case of dentition, oral epithelium invades the mesenchyme at the end of the second month of development. The cells within this epithelial invagination proliferate and maintain their continuity with the oral epithelium. This connection is the dental lamina. ■ **Fig. A** ■ The cells within the epithelium form a network of cells termed the stellate reticulum, which is lined internally by a layer of epithelial cells known as ameloblasts. ■ **Fig. B** ■ The stellate reticulum and the layer of ameloblasts together form the enamel organ.

Mesenchymal cells originally derived from the neural crest (see Core Concept 72) proliferate at the pole of the enamel organ opposite the dental lamina. ■ **Fig. B** ■ The enamel organ envelops this mesenchyme, which will become the dental pulp. In the third month ■ **Fig. C** ■, the ameloblast layer is located in close opposition to the odontoblast cell layer. The latter, a mesenchymal derivate, will give rise to the dentin.

As the tooth matures near term, both enamel and dentin are well organized. The dental lamina and the stellate reticulum both regress. By the time the tooth ruptures, it develops specialized attachments to the alveolar bone. These include a layer of cementoblast cells adjacent to the peripheral dentin and the periodontal ligament, which contains fibers between the cementoblast layer and the anchoring bone. ■ **Fig. D** ■

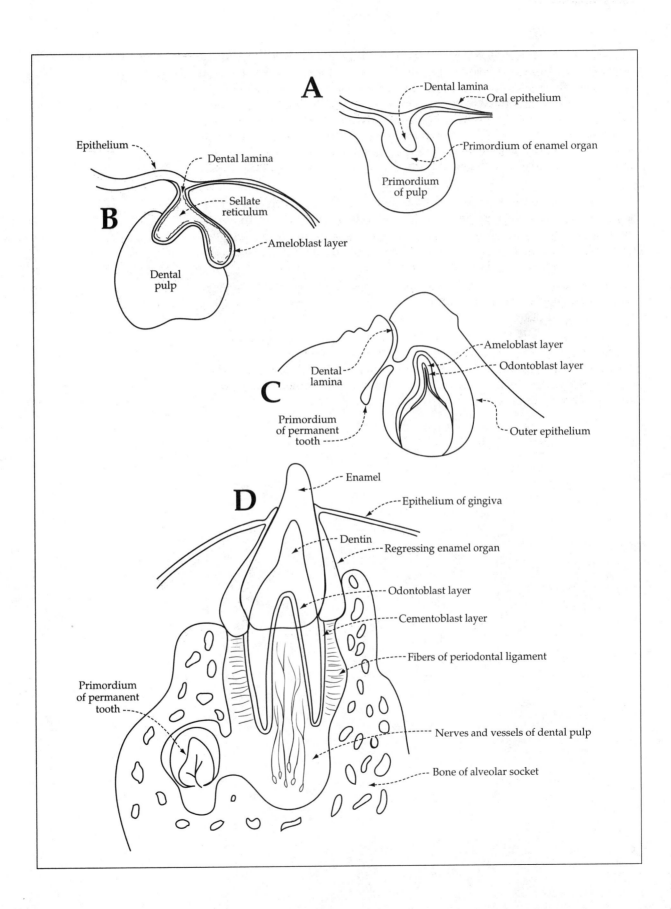

34 / Cardiogenic Mesoderm

The cardiovascular system begins development in the third week postfertilization. The primitive coelomic cavity, which forms between the somatic and splanchnic intraembryonic mesoderm, develops islands or clusters of cells on its splanchnic side destined to be the precursors of the cardiovascular system. These are the angiogenic cell clusters, which differentiate to form both endothelial cells and thereby blood vessels, as well as hematopoietic stem cells to populate the newly formed vessels. The angiogenic cell clusters are found in a horseshoe-shaped configuration lateral and rostral to the head of the presomite embryo. ■ **Fig. A** ■

As development proceeds, the inverted U-shaped angiogenic cell clusters begin to coalesce and form a primitive endothelial-lined blood vessel known as the endocardial tube. As seen in a cross-section through the neural plate, this tube is located between the splanchnic mesoderm and the underlying endoderm of the secondary yolk sac. ■ **Fig. B** ■

Further development of the cardiovascular system awaits the major foldings, which occur at the end of the third week, to transform the embryo from a flattened trilaminar disc to a flexed, cylindrical tube.

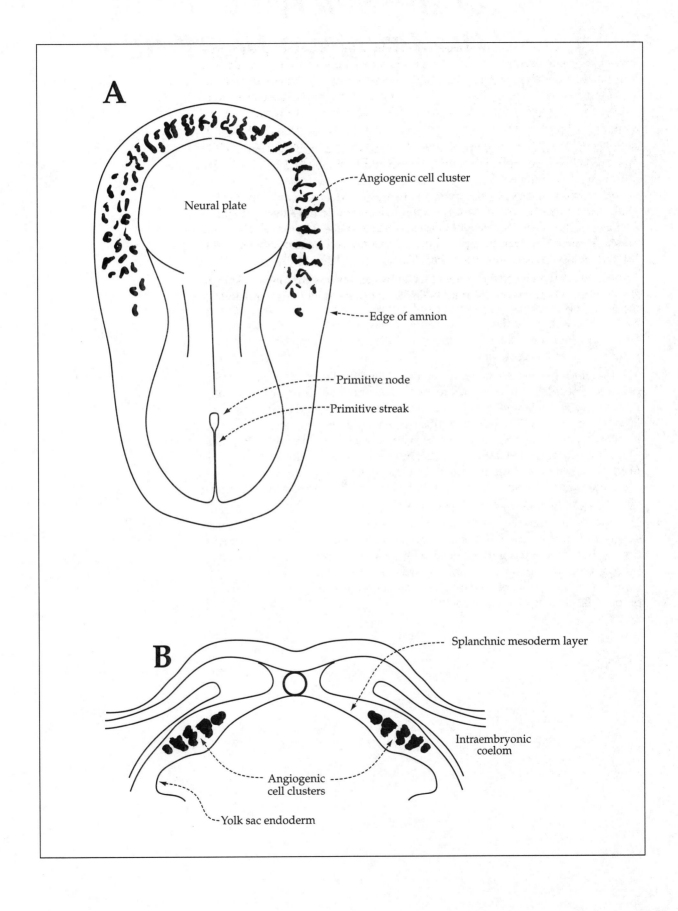

A

Neural plate

Angiogenic cell cluster

Edge of amnion

Primitive node

Primitive streak

B

Splanchnic mesoderm layer

Intraembryonic coelom

Angiogenic cell clusters

Yolk sac endoderm

35 / Ventral and Lateral Folding of the Embryo to Form the Primitive Heart Tube

As the horseshoe-shaped endocardial tube forms, the lateral-to-medial folding of the embryo brings the two parallel ends of the tube toward the ventral midline. The splanchnic mesoderm, closely associated with the endothelium of this tube, begins to synthesize and secrete large amounts of an extracellular matrix material known as cardiac jelly, which is interposed between the endocardial tube and the splanchnic mesoderm. ■ **Fig. A** ■ By this time the splanchnic mesoderm producing cardiac jelly is destined to become the myocardial component of the developing heart. Just lateral to the splanchnic mesoderm lies the intraembryonic coelom. This space is bordered laterally by the somatic mesoderm. As the somatic mesoderm continues to fold ventrally, the coelomic space, which was first located lateral to the endocardial tube, now surrounds the tube. This space continues to expand and is the pericardial coelom or cavity. ■ **Fig. B** ■ Because the entire coelomic cavity has not yet been partitioned (see Core Concepts 21 and 22), the pericardial cavity is initially continuous with the rest of the coelom.

The lateral-to-medial folding in the ventral midline finally brings the two limbs of the endocardial tube together to fuse. The primitive heart now contains three layers: an inner endocardium, an outer myocardium, and an intermediate layer of cardiac jelly. The heart is a tube suspended in the pericardial cavity by its attachment to the body of the embryo, the dorsal mesocardium. ■ **Fig. C** ■ The fourth layer of the developing heart, the epicardium, develops as cells from the dorsal mesocardium migrate ventrally to cover the surface of the myocardium. ■ **Fig. D** ■ Note that these folding events also help to form the primitive digestive system, located immediately dorsal to the developing heart.

The rostral-caudal folding of the endocardial tube swings the tube from a position rostral to the head ■ **Fig. E** ■ to one where it is located ventral to the embryonic body and inferior to the head. ■ **Fig. F** ■ In this position the heart may be considered to be a simple tube, connected at its rostral end by the aortic arches (see Core Concept 27) and at its caudal end primarily by blood vessels of the yolk sac (see Core Concept 38).

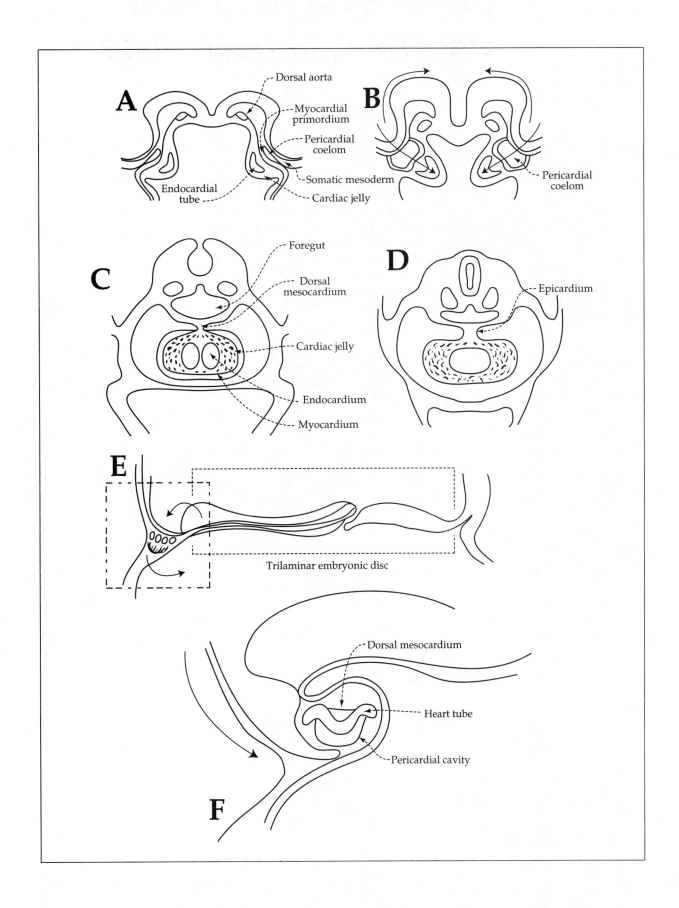

A — Dorsal aorta, Myocardial primordium, Pericardial coelom, Somatic mesoderm, Cardiac jelly, Endocardial tube

B — Pericardial coelom

C — Foregut, Dorsal mesocardium, Cardiac jelly, Endocardium, Myocardium

D — Epicardium

E — Trilaminar embryonic disc

F — Dorsal mesocardium, Heart tube, Pericardial cavity

36 / Establishment of the Primitive Heart Chamber Regions

The fusion of the endocardial heart tube proceeds both rostrally and caudally. **■ Fig. A ■** At its rostral end, the paired first aortic arches, which are continuous with the heart tube and rostral to the pericardial cavity, curve dorsally on either side of the buccopharyngeal membrane, or future mouth region. **■ Fig. B ■** These blood vessels course along the length of the dorsal body wall of the early embryo and hence are called the dorsal aortae.

Caudal to the aortic arch and within the pericardial cavity lies the primitive outflow tract of the heart. See **■ Fig. B ■** This region is termed the bulbus cordis. It will soon elongate and differentiate into a distal portion, the truncus arteriosus (see Core Concept 37). Caudal to the bulbus cordis is found the primitive ventricle, followed by the atrium, which is apparent even before the heart tube is fully fused on right and left halves. Finally, at the caudal border of the pericardial cavity, where it is in close proximity to the septum transversum, primitive blood vessels form in the local mesenchyme. These vessels coalesce and become continuous with the atrium on their proximal end and with the venous system of the embryo and yolk sac on the distal end. The confluence of this venous drainage, the sinus venosus, constitutes the inflow tract of the developing heart. Like the atrium, the sinus venosus appears bilaterally symmetrical in its early stages of development.

Each of these primitive regions of the developing heart is demarcated from each other by the proliferation of endocardial cushion tissue or endocardial swellings, which leave slight impressions on the ventral surface of the heart between the major developing regions. **■ Fig. C ■** This important mesenchymal tissue forms the precursor of valves and, in the case of the outflow tract, the precursor of septal tissue that separates systemic and pulmonary circulation (see Core Concept 40).

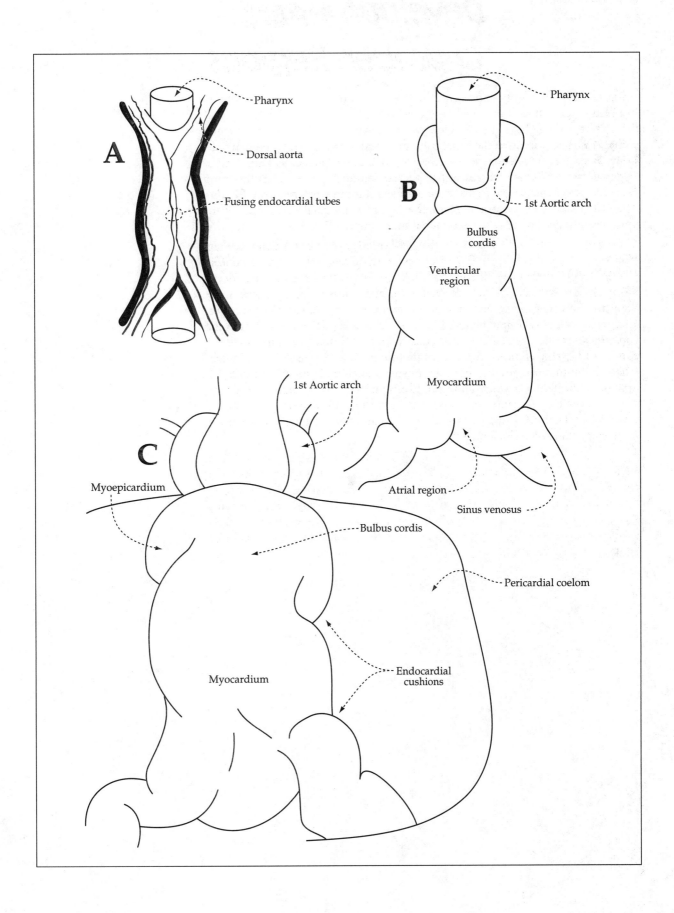

A

Pharynx

Dorsal aorta

Fusing endocardial tubes

B

Pharynx

1st Aortic arch

Bulbus cordis

Ventricular region

Myocardium

Atrial region

Sinus venosus

C

1st Aortic arch

Myoepicardium

Bulbus cordis

Pericardial coelom

Myocardium

Endocardial cushions

37 / Loop Phase of Heart Development

Because the inflow and the outflow tracts of the heart tube are relatively fixed in position, growth in the length of the tube is accompanied by a bulging of the tube to the right of the midline when viewed from the ventral aspect. ■ **Fig. A** ■ This looping of the tube, combined with its rapid elongation, results in the bending back of the tube so that its original orientation is altered. This is particularly evident with respect to the atrium and ventricle. The looping process swings the atrium from a caudal position to a position dorsal and rostral relative to the ventricle. ■ **Figs. B–D** ■ Concurrently, the outflow tract's extension gives rise to its three regionally distinct areas. ■ **Fig. E** ■ The distal area from which the aortic arches develop is the truncus arteriosus, which overlaps with the aortic bulb at its most distal end, and the conus cordis at the proximal end. A groove may be observed between the conus cordis and the ventricle known as the bulboventricular sulcus.

Thus, the human heart at the end of the first month of development takes on an appearance approximating the adult heart. See ■ **Fig. E** ■ Viewed from the ventral aspect, the apex of the heart consists of the primitive ventricle and the conus cordis. The left and right sides of the primitive atrium are separated ventrally by the unpartitioned truncus arteriosus. The dorsal aspect of the developing heart will be considered in Core Concept 38.

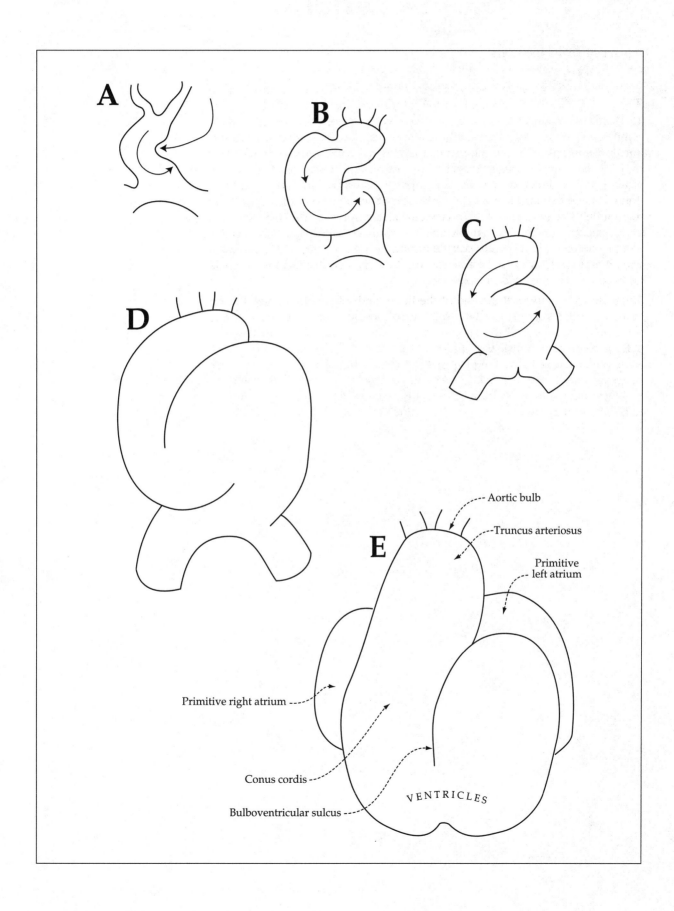

A

B

C

D

E

Aortic bulb

Truncus arteriosus

Primitive
left atrium

Primitive right atrium

Conus cordis

Bulboventricular sulcus

VENTRICLES

38 / Sinus Venosus Development

Having surveyed the overall early anatomy of the developing heart from the ventral aspect in the previous plate, we will now consider the heart from the dorsal side. The key event occurring here from the end of the first month through the second month is the development of the sinus venosus.

The sinus venosus is the inflow tract of the heart and comprises two bilaterally symmetrical sinus horns that empty into the common atrium at the sinoatrial junction. ■ **Fig. A** ■ The sinus horns themselves are made up of the confluence of the three major venous systems of the embryo: (1) the systemic venous network, which includes the anterior and posterior cardinal veins and their junction just lateral to each sinus horn, which form the common cardinal veins; (2) the umbilical veins, medial to the common cardinal veins; and (3) the vitelline, or omphalomesenteric veins, medial to the umbilical veins. Both of these latter venous systems are involved with the establishment of nutritional circulation via the umbilical cord and the yolk sac, respectively. Development of their distal portions is considered in Core Concept 44.

The basic symmetry of the sinus venosus and the three venous networks becomes greatly modified after the first month of development. In effect, the right horn predominates, and the opening of the sinus venosus shifts to the right side of the atrium. ■ **Fig. B** ■ The right umbilical vein is obliterated, and the right vitelline vein forms the proximal portion of the inferior vena cava. The proximal superior vena cava is formed from the right common cardinal and anterior cardinal vein. ■ **Fig. C** ■ The greatly reduced left sinus horn develops into the coronary sinus and the small oblique vein of the left atrium. ■ **Fig. D** ■

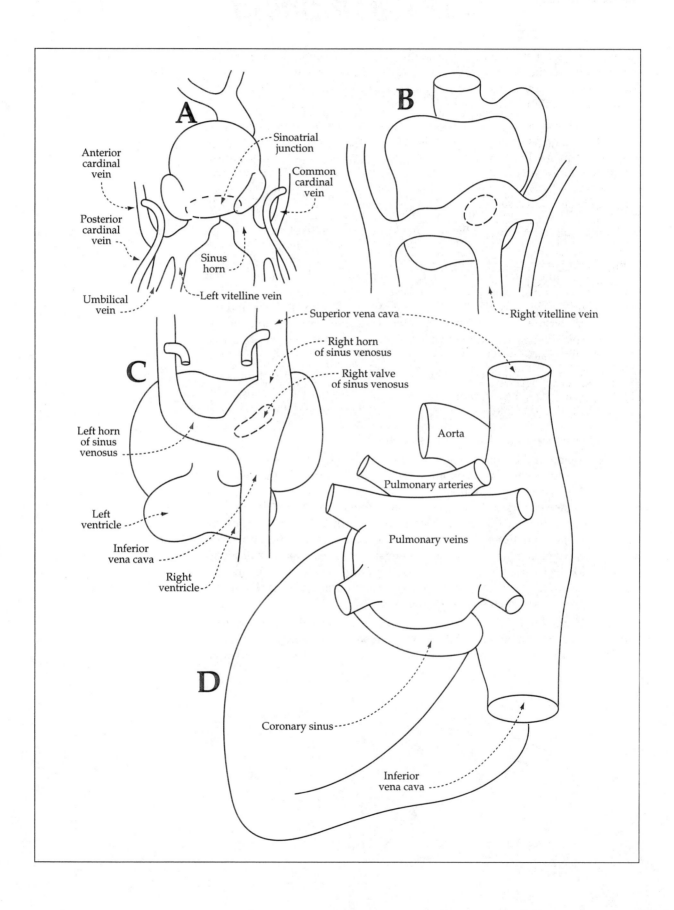

A

Anterior cardinal vein

Sinoatrial junction

Common cardinal vein

Posterior cardinal vein

Sinus horn

Umbilical vein

Left vitelline vein

B

Right vitelline vein

C

Superior vena cava

Right horn of sinus venosus

Right valve of sinus venosus

Left horn of sinus venosus

Left ventricle

Inferior vena cava

Right ventricle

Aorta

Pulmonary arteries

Pulmonary veins

D

Coronary sinus

Inferior vena cava

39 / Atrial Development and Partitioning

With the inflow tract shifted to the right side of the atrium, development of the atrium, which takes place during the second month after fertilization, may be appreciated by viewing a coronal section of the heart. The two major processes that occur simultaneously — the actual differentiation of the atrium and the partitioning of the single atrium into right and left chambers — will be described separately.

The inflow tract joins the right side of the atrium to form the sinoatrial orifice. ■ **Fig. A** ■ This elongated opening has a left and right border, termed the sinoatrial valves, and a small appendage at its cranial end, known as the septum spurium. As the heart grows, a substantial portion of the sinus venosus becomes incorporated into the wall of the right side of the atrium. This phenomenon, termed intussusception, results in the formation of the smooth-walled sinus venarum. ■ **Fig. B** ■ Near the caudal margin of the sinus venarum, the right sinoatrial valve develops into the valve of the inferior vena cava and the valve of the coronary sinus, and the crista terminalis becomes evident. The latter represents the demarcation between the sinus venarum and the rough, or trabeculated, remainder of the right atrium.

The left side of the atrium is also greatly modified by the process of intussusception. See ■ **Fig. B** ■ In this case, veins form in the mesenchyme in the vicinity of the developing lung. These vessels become incorporated into the wall of the left atrium. Four such veins normally form, leaving most of this portion at the atrium smooth walled like the sinus venarum.

The partitioning of the primitive atrium into separate chambers is initiated by the downward growth of the septum primum, which forms a curtainlike barrier from the cranial border of the atrium to the endocardial cushion tissue at the junction between the atrium and primitive ventricle. ■ **Fig. C** ■ The last part of the septum primum to close is located near the cushion tissue and is called the foramen primum. Before the septum primum completely closes, however, a series of perforations appear near its cranial end. These soon coalesce to form the foramen secundum. Now a second septum, the septum secundum, develops just to the right and parallel to the septum primum. It grows downward to cover the foramen secundum only partially.

The higher pressure on the right side of the heart in utero allows the septum primum to act as a unidirectional flutter valve to shunt blood from the right to the left atrium, thus acting to bypass the high-resistance pulmonary circulation.

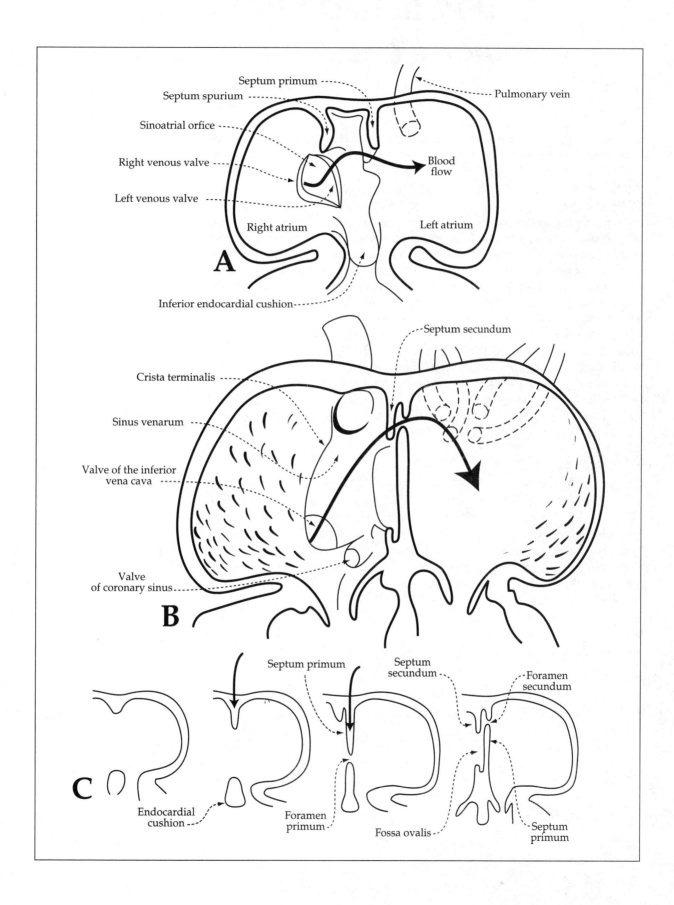

A

Septum primum
Septum spurium
Sinoatrial orfice
Right venous valve
Left venous valve
Right atrium
Inferior endocardial cushion
Pulmonary vein
Blood flow
Left atrium

B

Septum secundum
Crista terminalis
Sinus venarum
Valve of the inferior vena cava
Valve of coronary sinus

C

Septum primum
Septum secundum
Foramen secundum
Endocardial cushion
Foramen primum
Fossa ovalis
Septum primum

40 / Ventricular Partitioning and the Formation of the Aorticopulmonary Septum

The partitioning of the primitive ventricle into the right and left ventricles is a complex process intimately associated with the separation of the outflow tract into the aorta and pulmonary artery. Although they occur simultaneously during the second month of development, here they will be considered separately.

Ventricular partitioning takes place by the ultimate fusion of two embryologically separate septa that form between the primitive ventricle. By the beginning of the second month, a thick, muscular interventricular septum grows from the apex of the heart toward the common outflow tract. ■ **Fig. A** ■ The rostral free edge of this muscular portion of the septum encounters atrioventricular cushion tissue, which has proliferated from the inferior aspect of the atrioventricular canal. At the same time the outflow tract develops a pair of internal ridges that grow toward each other all along the outflow tract from the conus cordis to the truncus arteriosus. These ridges are known as the left and right bulbar or truncoconal ridges. As the bulbar ridges come together in the proximal part of the outflow tract, they also grow toward each other all along the length of the truncus arteriosus as well. As they do so, the two ridges execute a 180-degree spiral to form the aorticopulmonary, or spiral, septum. This septum separates the pulmonary trunk that crosses the heart ventrally from the right ventricle and the aorta, now connected exclusively with the left ventricle and passing posterior to the pulmonary artery.

The truncoconal ridges meet at the proximal end of the outflow tract together with the inferior atrioventricular cushion to form the membranous part of the interventricular septum. ■ **Fig. B** ■ The multicomponent membranous septum finally fuses with the muscular septum to form the complete interventricular septum.

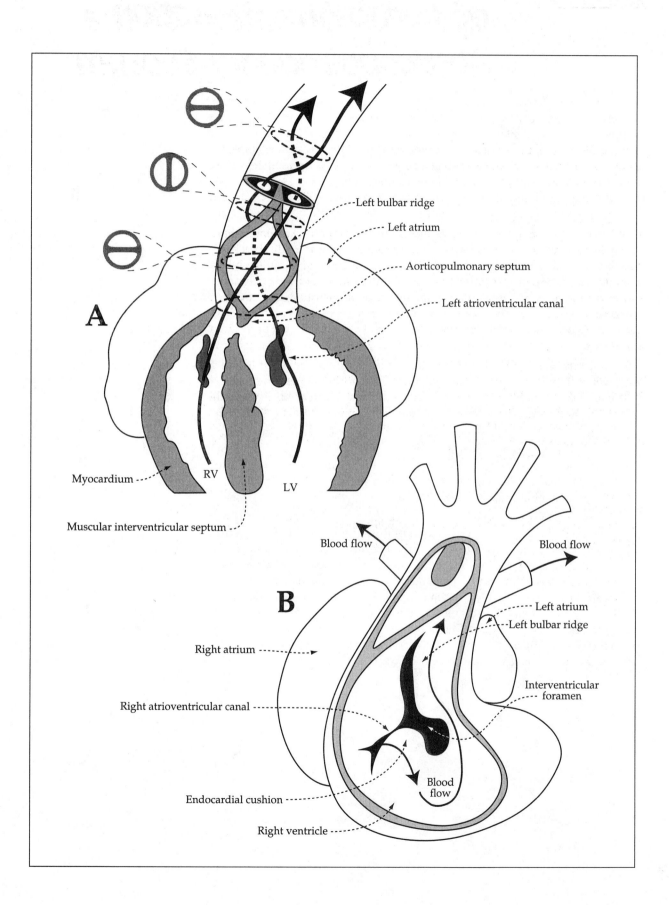

A

Left bulbar ridge

Left atrium

Aorticopulmonary septum

Left atrioventricular canal

Myocardium

RV

LV

Muscular interventricular septum

B

Blood flow

Blood flow

Left atrium
Left bulbar ridge

Right atrium

Interventricular foramen

Right atrioventricular canal

Blood flow

Endocardial cushion

Right ventricle

41 / Common Anomalies of Aortic Arch Selection

Heart congenital anomalies are the most frequently encountered embryologic defects. These anomalies may be generally subdivided into those based on abnormalities in the development of the fourth aortic arch and those based on abnormalities in the development of the heart itself. Only a few examples of these anomalies will be described here. We will first consider anomalies of aortic arch selection.

In the normal situation, the proximal portion of the left fourth arch is retained as part of the aortic arch. The left fourth arch becomes the proximal left subclavian, and its distal segment arises from the seventh intersegmental artery. This pattern is generated by the specific obliteration of the arterial segment between the seventh intersegmental artery and the right dorsal aorta just before it joins its counterpart on the left side to form the unpaired descending aorta (see Core Concept 27). When this obliteration occurs with the left dorsal aortic segment rather than the right, a right aortic arch develops, with the innominate artery occurring on the left side. This anomaly is termed right aortic arch. ■ **Fig. A** ■

When the arterial segment that is obliterated consists of the right fourth arch to the level of the seventh intersegmental artery, that is, the segment proximal to that which is normally obliterated, the right subclavian artery arises from the arch of the aorta and passes posterior to the trachea and esophagus. ■ **Fig. B** ■

Should the entire fourth arch persist instead of undergoing normal obliteration of the distal right segment, an aortic arch develops on both the left and right sides. This anomaly, known as double aortic arch, is characterized by the presence of a vascular ring around the trachea and esophagus made up of the retained right and left aortic arches. ■ **Fig. C** ■

Finally, instead of a complete obliteration of an arterial segment that is normally retained, the etiology of coarctation of the aorta is thought to stem from the partial obliteration or constriction of the left distal aortic arch. This coarctation usually occurs just distal to the ductus arteriosus (see Core Concept 45). Such a postductal coarctation of the aorta may result in unusual compensatory circulatory pathways by which systemic blood is brought to the regions inferior to the coarctation. For example, the left subclavian may anastomose with the internal thoracic artery and finally by way of dilated intersegmental arteries to the descending aorta. Such patterns demonstrate the high degree of plasticity of the developing vascular system. ■ **Fig. D** ■

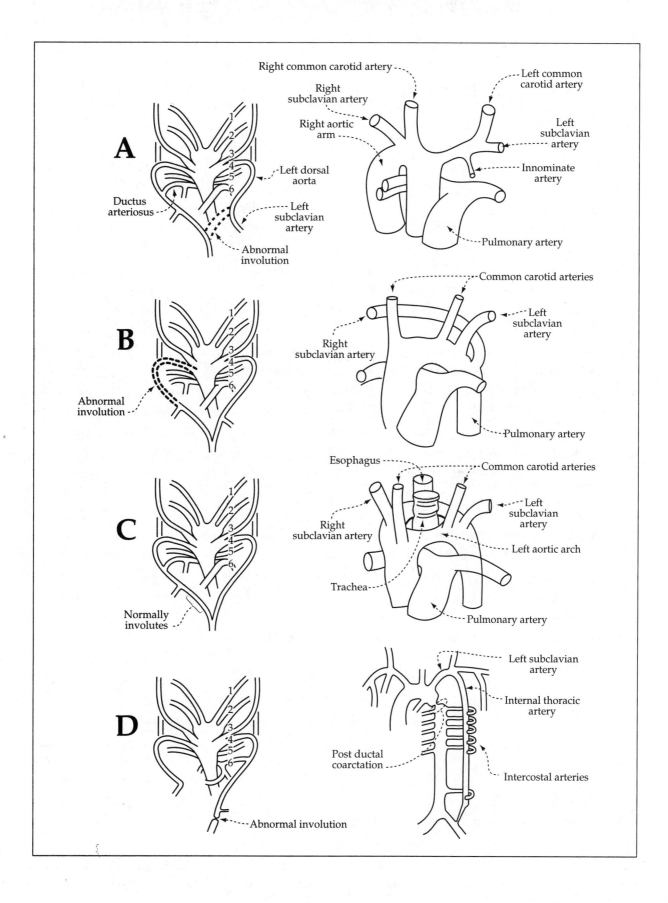

42 / Common Anomalies of Heart Development

Of the myriad specific congenital heart defects, most can be classified into a few embryologically based categories. A few examples of major anomalies intrinsic to heart development will be described.

Atrial septal defects (ASDs) arise as defects in the formation of either of the two septa that develop parallel to one another and divide the primitive atrium, or in the two foramina that sequentially appear in the septum primum. If the foramen secundum is too large or the septum secundum does not grow far enough inferiorly, a patency is maintained between the two atria. ■ **Fig. A1** ■ When the endocardial cushion tissue at the atrioventricular junction does not proliferate properly, the septum primum may not grow far enough inferiorly to meet the cushion tissue, resulting in a persistent foramen primum. ■ **Fig. A2** ■ Because the endocardial cushions are also involved in the formation of the atrioventricular valves, this defect is usually accompanied by malformations in the bicuspid valve. Rare forms of ASD stem from the failure of normal intrassuseption of the sinus venosus into the primitive atrium.

Ventricular septal defects (VSDs) can arise as either defects in the muscular ventricular septum or, much more commonly, the membranous septum. The failure of the conotruncal ridges and inferior atrioventricular cushion tissue to fuse together properly forms the basis of this anomaly. ■ **Fig. B** ■

Closely related embryologically to VSDs are anomalies of the partitioning of the outflow tract. If the right and left conotruncal ridges do not form or do not close, a persistent truncus arteriosus will result. ■ **Fig. C** ■ Since the conotruncal ridges develop abnormally, this defect is typically accompanied by a VSD. The pulmonary trunk is greatly reduced or even absent in such a defect. When no pulmonary artery develops, the lungs are supplied by dilated bronchial arteries. Finally, in cases where the conotruncal ridges fuse but do not execute the normal 180-degree spiral, the resulting anomaly is termed transposition of the great vessels. Shunts between the systemic and pulmonary circulation must be established to permit survival. ■ **Fig. D** ■

A narrowing, or stenosis, of the pulmonary or aortic semilunar valves may occur when the conotruncal ridges do not divide the outflow tract equally at the level of the developing valves. Valve cusps may fuse with one another, resulting in poor mechanical function. ■ **Fig. E** ■

Because the events of heart development are interrelated, defects often present as a series of anomalies. A common example is tetralogy of Fallot, characterized by a VSD, overriding aorta, right ventricular hypertrophy, and pulmonary stenosis.

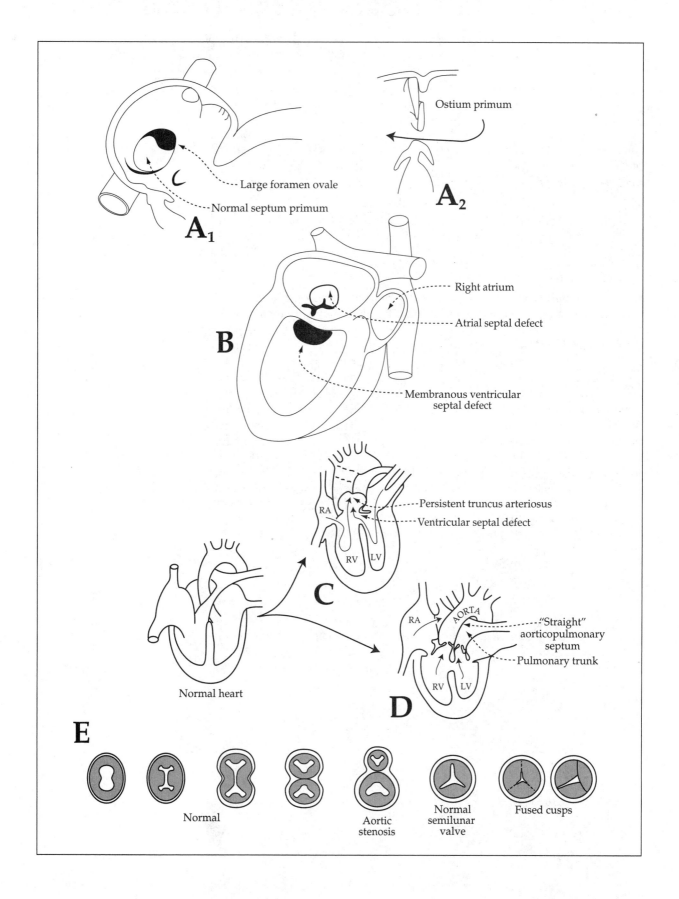

Ostium primum

Large foramen ovale

Normal septum primum

A₁

A₂

B

Right atrium

Atrial septal defect

Membranous ventricular
septal defect

C

RA

Persistent truncus arteriosus

Ventricular septal defect

RV   LV

Normal heart

D

RA   AORTA

"Straight"
aorticopulmonary
septum

Pulmonary trunk

RV   LV

E

Normal

Aortic
stenosis

Normal
semilunar
valve

Fused cusps

43 / Embryonic Circulation and Development of the Arterial System

By the end of the first month of development, the embryo has established a functional circulatory system that includes two separate nutrition networks, the vitelline and umbilical system, as well as a system intrinsic to the embryo itself. ■ **Fig. A** ■ As the nutrition networks develop, the vitelline system becomes less prominent in its circulatory role as the umbilical system assumes more of this function. Both nutrition networks are connected to the embryo by way of the dorsal aorta, with the vitelline artery meeting the dorsal aorta at the level of the midbody and the umbilical artery meeting it near its caudal end. Note that the umbilical artery carries relatively unoxygenated blood and metabolic waste products from the embryo to the chorion.

The main arterial system of the embryo proper includes the aortic arch system, which has been described in Core Concept 27, and segmental branches of the dorsal aorta. These branches may be considered organized in a simple regional distribution. ■ **Fig. B** ■ Dorsal branches proceed toward the developing spinal cord, supplying blood to this area, and giving additional segmental arteries that pass between the developing ribs as the intercostal arteries. The lateral branches are more prominent in the early embryo since they supply the segmentally arranged mesonephros (see Core Concept 57). These arteries lose their segmental organization with the ascent of the metanephros and ultimately give rise to the definitive renal arteries. Finally, the ventral segmental arteries are initially associated with the broad yolk sac in early development. With the development of the digestive system, these paired blood vessels fuse in the midventral line and regionally supply the developing gut. The resulting adult derivatives of this group include the celiac artery and the superior and inferior mesenteric arteries. ■ **Fig. C** ■

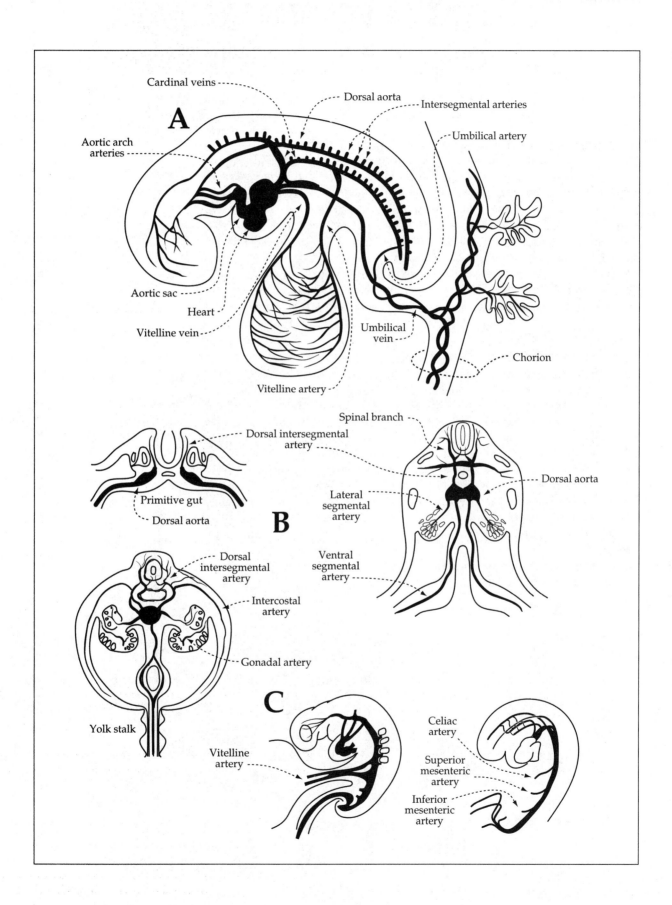

44 / Scheme for the Development of the Venous System

The venous system of the embryo proper consists of the paired left and right anterior and posterior cardinal veins, which come together to form the left and right common cardinal veins. These empty into their respective sinus horns. ■ **Fig. A** ■ The basic pattern for the rest of venous system development bears a similarity to the organization of the arterial system at its earliest stages in that there are paired vitelline veins, situated medial to paired umbilical veins. This nutritional venous system empties into the sinus venous but is soon modified by the interposition of the rapidly growing liver (see Core Concept 51) inferior to the sinus venosus. See ■ **Fig. A** ■ The vitelline veins break up into an anastomosing complex of sinusoids within the growing liver parenchyma. ■ **Fig. B** ■ At their proximal end, the right vitelline vein's connection to the sinus venosus enlarges, while the left one diminishes. ■ **Fig. C** ■ A channel, or shunt, is thus formed through the embryonic liver, emerging at its distal end as the left umbilical vein. This venous shunt is the ductus venosus. ■ **Fig. D** ■ The right proximal segment develops into a portion of the inferior vena cava (hepatic portion), and the distal portions of the vitelline veins contribute to the developing hepatic portal system.

Meanwhile, at the end of the first month of development, an anastomosing network of veins forms medial to the posterior cardinal veins. ■ **Fig. E1** ■ These are the subcardinal veins. Eventually they anastomose with one another near the midline of the embryo to form a portion of the inferior vena cava by way of an intersubcardinal anastomosis. ■ **Fig. E2** ■ By this time, both the original posterior cardinal and subcardinal systems are breaking down, and a new paired venous system, the supracardinal veins, is developing. The supracardinals connect the proximal remnants of the posterior cardinal vein to its distal remnant known as the iliac anastomosis. The supracardinal system ultimately develops into the azygos system of veins, draining the thoracic wall. ■ **Fig. E3** ■ The anterior cardinal system will give rise to the jugular and subclavian veins and a portion of the superior vena cava on the right side. A new anastomosis between the two anterior cardinal veins develops, which will form the proximal part of the left branchiocephalic vein.

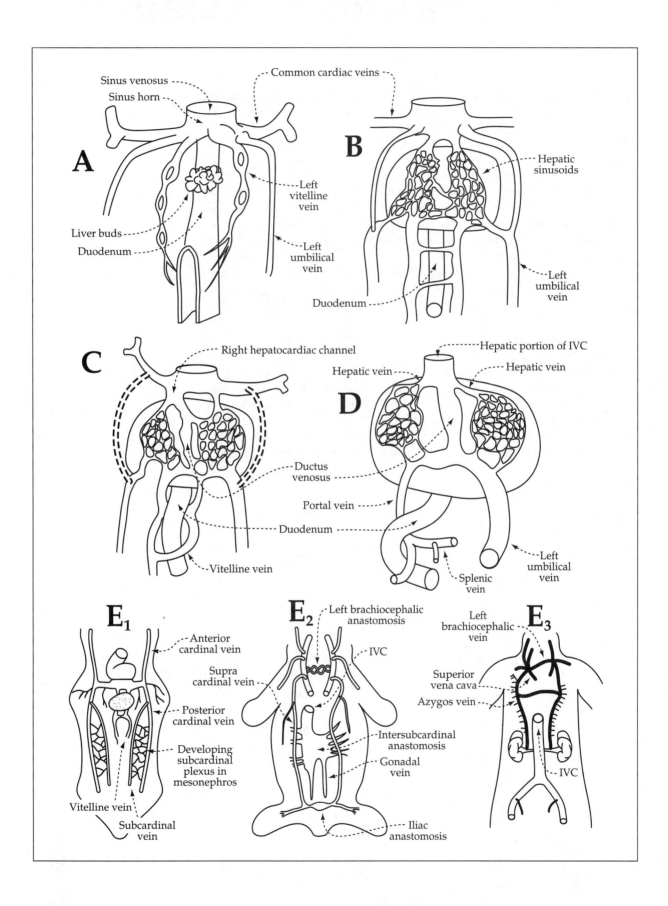

45 / Changes in Fetal Circulation After Birth

Because the placenta functions as both an embryonic lung for respiratory exchange and as an embryonic liver for a host of nutritional and metabolic purposes, these two major organs are largely bypassed in fetal circulation. Oxygenated blood arriving via the umbilical vein passes mostly through the ductus venosus, the inferior vena cava, and, finally, the right atrium. The higher pulmonary pressure permits most of this blood to bypass the lungs by streaming across the foramen ovale into the left atrium. The blood pumped out of the right ventricle also largely bypasses the lungs by being shunted into the descending aorta via the ductus arteriosus. Finally, circulation through the systemic system is brought back to the placenta by way of the umbilical arteries.
■ **Fig. A** ■

At birth, pulmonary resistance drops precipitously, and systemic pressure exceeds pulmonary pressure during all phases of the cardiac cycle. The umbilical vein soon becomes obliterated and survives as the ligamentum teres. The ductus venosus becomes significantly constricted and is now termed the ligamentum venosum. The foramen ovale is functionally closed because of the blood pressure reversal at birth; it usually becomes anatomically closed as well by fusing to the wall of the atrium to form the fossa ovalis. Following birth, the ductus arteriosus also becomes constricted, ultimately leaving a fibrous cord between the pulmonary artery and the aorta, the ligamentum arteriosum. Finally, the umbilical arteries are obliterated at their distal ends, forming the medial umbilical ligaments and leaving their proximal portions, the superior vesicle arteries, still functioning as a major blood supply to the bladder.
■ **Fig. B** ■

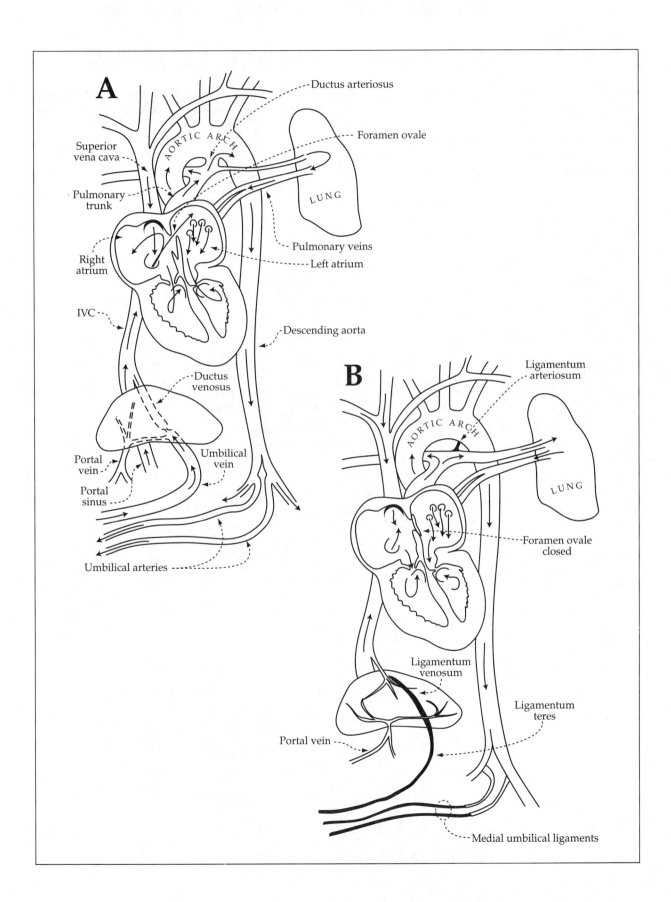

A

Ductus arteriosus

Foramen ovale

Superior
vena cava

AORTIC ARCH

LUNG

Pulmonary
trunk

Pulmonary veins

Right
atrium

Left atrium

IVC

Descending aorta

Ductus
venosus

B

Ligamentum
arteriosum

AORTIC ARCH

LUNG

Portal
vein

Umbilical
vein

Foramen ovale
closed

Portal
sinus

Umbilical arteries

Ligamentum
venosum

Ligamentum
teres

Portal vein

Medial umbilical ligaments

46 / Early Formation of the Different Regions of the Primitive Gastrointestinal System Based on Embryonic Folding

As the broad expanse of the secondary yolk sac begins to constrict and draw the embryo into its rostral-caudal folding along the ventral surface (also see Core Concepts 9 and 35), the early GI system initiates overt development in the fourth week postfertilization. The GI system always maintains some form of continuity with the yolk sac. Before this connection becomes very narrow, the region of the gut anterior to the border of the yolk sac is known as the foregut. The foregut is continuous anteriorly with the primitive pharynx and is bordered anteriorly by the buccopharyngeal membrane and posteriorly by the anterior intestinal portal. Similarly, the embryologic hindgut is defined as the region of the gut bordered posteriorly by the cloacal membrane and anteriorly by its continuity with the yolk sac, the posterior intestinal portal. Note the allantois, a diverticulum of the hindgut. The middle expanse of the developing gut, not closed off but rapidly narrowing, is the midgut. ■ **Fig. A** ■

With development, the regional portions of the GI system become precisely defined anatomically. The foregut extends to a major diverticulum from which the pancreas and liver emerge (see Core Concepts 50 and 51). The hindgut begins at the distal third of the future transverse colon. In between, the midgut develops ■ **Fig. B** ■ as detailed later (see Core Concept 52). These anatomic demarcations are also established by the specific arterial blood supply to the various portions of the gut. The foregut is supplied by the short celiac trunk, the midgut by the superior mesenteric artery, and the hindgut by the inferior mesenteric artery. ■ **Fig. C** ■ In this section, these embryologic concepts are presented in more detail.

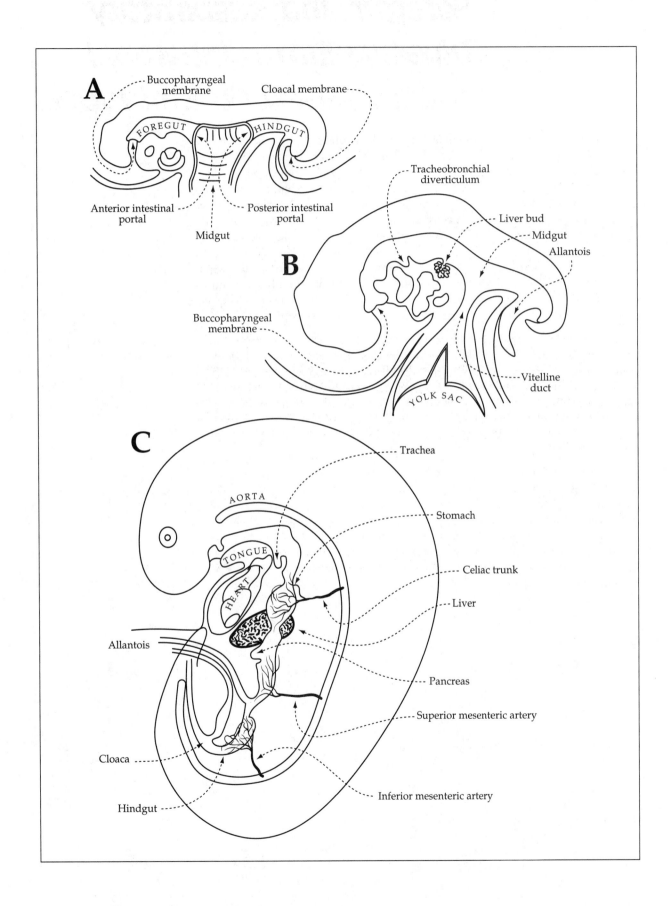

47 / Development of the Foregut and Respiratory Diverticulum

By the sixth week of development, the foregut is undergoing major changes. The formerly straight tube formed by the incorporation of the anterior portion of the yolk sac into the anterior ventral body wall has now developed a diverticulum, the trachea, off its ventral surface, which is expanding inferiorly and laterally. ■ **Fig. A** ■ The part of the foregut from which the diverticulum arises is now properly termed the pharynx, and the distal end of the diverticulum develops into the lung bud. ■ **Fig. B** ■ As the lung bud grows, its connection to the pharynx is a pair of long lateral grooves that grow toward each other to form the tracheoesophageal septum. This important partition completely separates the newly formed trachea and distal lung bud from the pharynx and its continuation, the esophagus. Failure of this partition to form normally results in a variety of relatively common anomalies (see Core Concept 49).

As lung development proceeds, the trachea branches into a right and left primary bronchus. These bronchi undergo dichotomous divisions as they grow into the surrounding splanchnic mesenchyme. ■ **Fig. C** ■ The developmental interaction between the epithelium of the bronchial tree and the mesenchyme results in the histologic and functional maturation of the lung. Such processes, known as epithelial-mesenchymal interactions, are common occurrences in embryology and have been referred to in the dentition developmental system (see Core Concept 33).

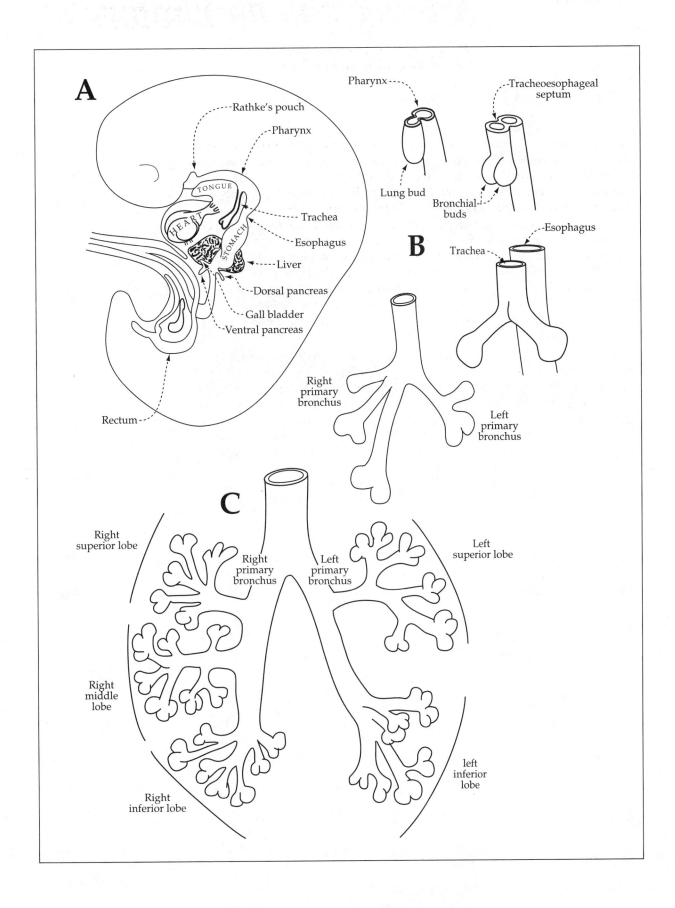

A

Rathke's pouch
Pharynx
TONGUE
HEART
STOMACH
Trachea
Esophagus
Liver
Dorsal pancreas
Gall bladder
Ventral pancreas
Rectum

Pharynx
Tracheoesophageal septum
Lung bud
Bronchial buds
B
Esophagus
Trachea
Right primary bronchus
Left primary bronchus

C
Right superior lobe
Right primary bronchus
Left primary bronchus
Left superior lobe
Right middle lobe
Right inferior lobe
left inferior lobe

48 / Histologic Development of the Lung and Esophagus

Histodifferentiation of the lung occurs in a series of specific stages. The earliest stage is called the pseudoglandular stage. The branching bronchi maintain a continuous columnar epithelium, their terminal portions end in rather simple blind sacs, and the surrounding mesenchyme has not yet undergone overt differentiation. ■ **Fig. A** ■ This stage is present well into the second trimester of development. Continuing through the end of the second trimester is the canalicular phase of lung development. ■ **Fig. B** ■ The terminal ends of the bronchi are now characterized by a ciliated cuboidal epithelium and are properly termed terminal bronchioles. They branch extensively to form respiratory bronchioles, which also have a continuous layer of cuboidal epithelium. Blood and lymphatic capillaries are now a prominent feature of the mesenchyme, although these capillaries have not yet established a close anatomic association with the bronchiole apparatus. The third phase of lung development occurs over the third trimester and is termed the terminal sac phase. ■ **Fig. C** ■ The cells of the terminal portions of the respiratory tree now become greatly attenuated in the form of a very thin squamous epithelium. Capillaries make intimate contact with these terminal sacs to form the functionally important alveolocapillary membrane. In the final stage of development, which lasts almost to adolescence, the capillaries appear to bulge into the terminal sacs to begin forming the mature alveoli. This fourth phase is called the alveolar period. ■ **Fig. D** ■

The development of the esophagus is characterized by the development of a thick, stratified, epithelial-lined lumen that becomes occluded during the second month of development and is recanalized shortly after by the coalescence of individual vacuoles. ■ **Fig. E** ■ By midterm, the esophagus has developed the mucosa, submucosa, muscularis, and adventitia characteristic of its mature histology. ■ **Fig. F** ■

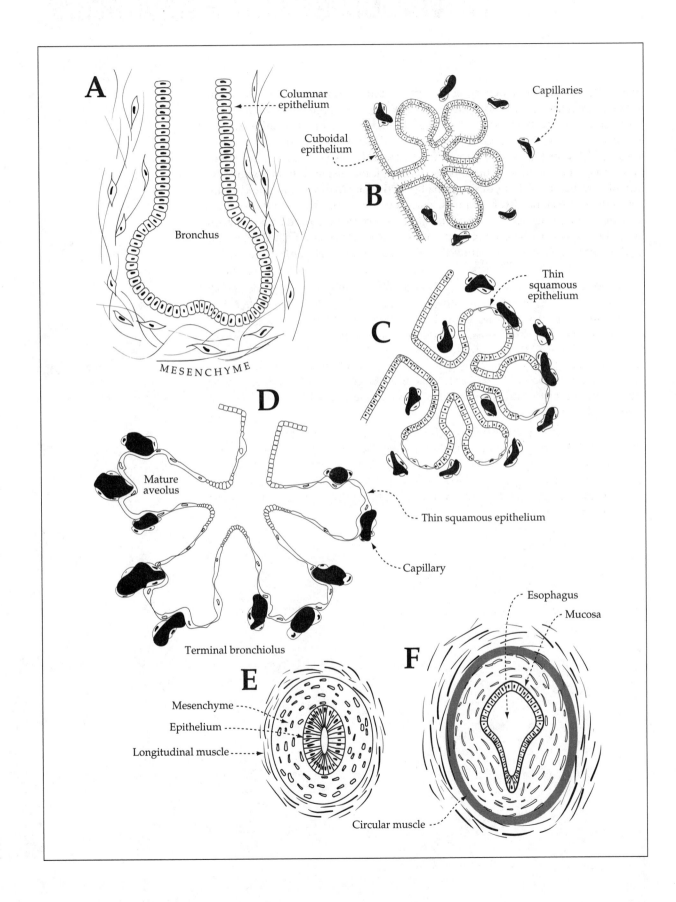

A — Columnar epithelium — Bronchus — MESENCHYME

B — Cuboidal epithelium — Capillaries

C — Thin squamous epithelium

D — Mature aveolus — Thin squamous epithelium — Capillary — Terminal bronchiolus

E — Mesenchyme — Epithelium — Longitudinal muscle

F — Esophagus — Mucosa — Circular muscle

49 / Anomalies of Foregut Development

The failure of the tracheoesophageal septum to form normally often results in a condition termed tracheoesophageal fistula. In the large majority of these cases, the esophagus ends as a blind pouch, that is, undergoes atresia, and the distal esophageal segment is directly connected, or forms a fistula, with the trachea. ■ **Fig. A** ■ Such a condition would obviously result in the regurgitation of saliva and food on first feeding, as well as the distention of the bowel during breathing. Variations of this anomaly include a proximal fistula and distal esophageal atresia. ■ **Fig. B** ■ In this case, air cannot reach the bowel, but food is aspirated into the lungs. In addition, a common fistula may occur between the esophagus and the trachea without esophageal atresia. ■ **Fig. C** ■ Finally, the atretic esophagus may form a tracheoesophageal fistula at both its proximal and distal ends. ■ **Fig. D** ■

An anomaly of esophageal development is the narrowing, or stenosis, of the esophageal lumen. Esophageal stenosis is thought to result from the inability of the esophagus to undergo normal recanalization following its brief occlusion phase early in development (see Core Concept 48).

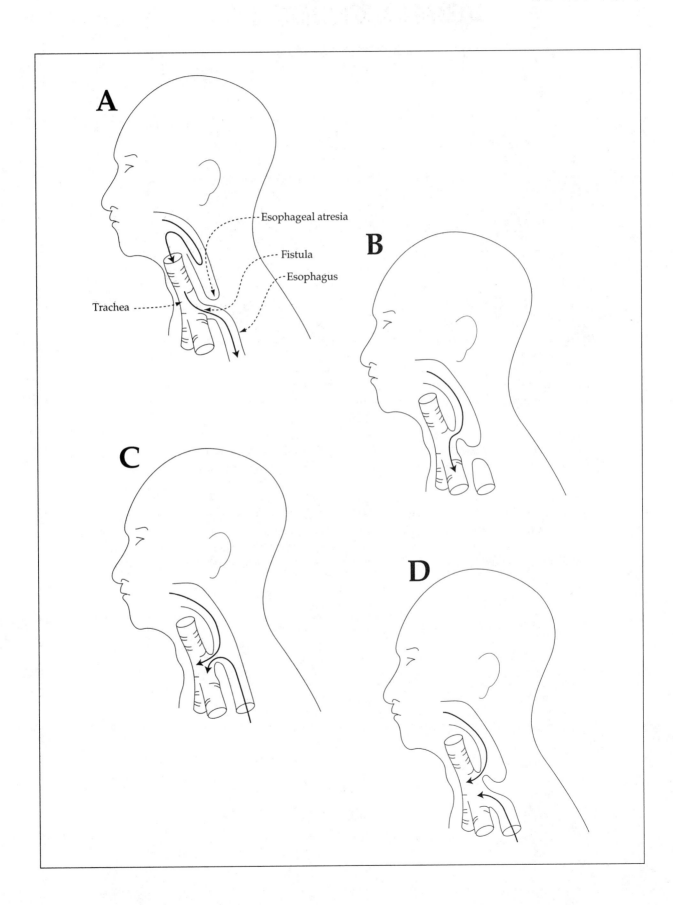

A

Esophageal atresia

Fistula

Esophagus

Trachea

B

C

D

50 Development of the Stomach, Spleen, and Pancreas

The most distal part of the foregut is the stomach and proximal duodenum. The development of the stomach may be traced from the fourth week postfertilization, at which time a slight dorsal dilation in the gut tube is observed. ■ **Fig. A** ■ As this dilation becomes more pronounced, the developing stomach undergoes a 90-degree rotation around two axes. In the first rotation, the former ventral surface of the stomach tube comes to lie on the right side and becomes the lesser curvature, and the former dorsal surface, as the greater curvature, comes to lie on the left. ■ **Fig. B** ■ The second rotation occurs in a clockwise direction to shift the superior, or cardiac, region of the stomach to the left and the inferior, or pyloric, region to the right. ■ **Fig. C** ■

Like the rest of the digestive tube, the stomach is originally suspended in the coelomic cavity by a dorsal and ventral mesentery (mesogastrium). The important dorsal mesentery not only serves as the medium through which the celiac artery supplies this part of the foregut, but also the substrate on which the spleen and most of the pancreas develop. The spleen arises from mesenchymal precursor cells located in the dorsal mesentery. ■ **Fig. B** ■ The mesenchyme forms the parenchyma, stroma, and capsule of the spleen, which then become infiltrated with hematopoetic cells. ■ **Fig. D** ■ This organ is supplied by the large splenic artery, a major branch of the celiac trunk. The pancreas also grows in the mesogastrium, but unlike the spleen, it develops from two primordia, which emerge as diverticula off the duodenum. See ■ **Figs. A–C** ■ The point at which these diverticula arise defines the embryologic border between the proximal foregut and the distal midgut. The small ventral diverticulum swings around dorsally to fuse with the larger dorsal pancreas. See ■ **Fig. D** ■ Their connections to the duodenum normally also fuse to form the pancreatic duct. The entire pancreas takes up a retroperitoneal position and is supplied by branches of both the celiac trunk and the superior mesenteric artery.

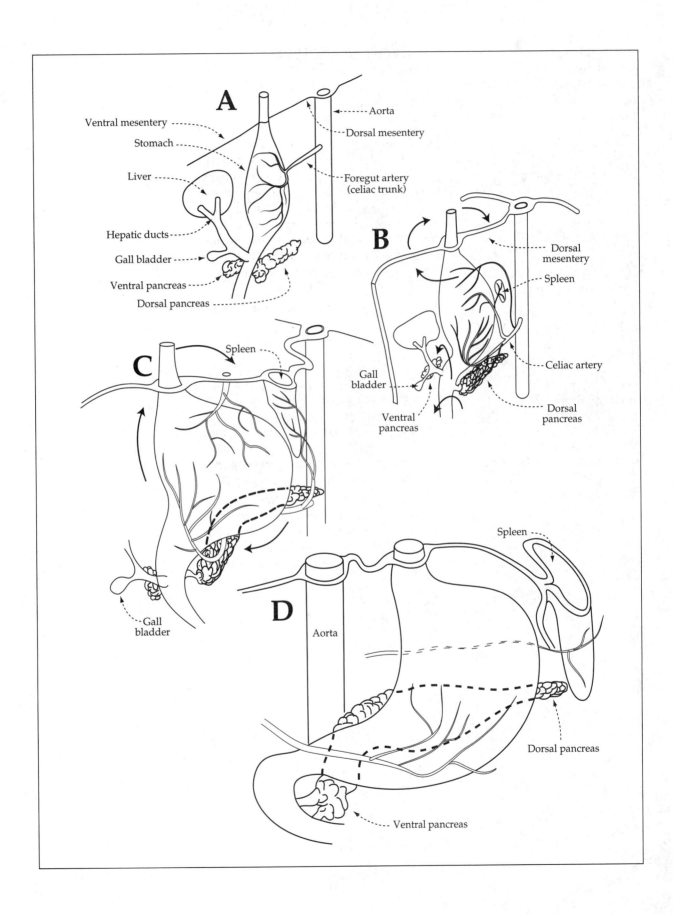

A

Ventral mesentery

Stomach

Liver

Hepatic ducts

Gall bladder

Ventral pancreas

Dorsal pancreas

Aorta

Dorsal mesentery

Foregut artery
(celiac trunk)

B

Dorsal
mesentery

Spleen

Celiac artery

Gall
bladder

Ventral
pancreas

Dorsal
pancreas

C

Spleen

Gall
bladder

D

Aorta

Spleen

Dorsal pancreas

Ventral pancreas

51 / Development of the Liver

By the middle of the fourth week of development, a diverticulum off the gut tube at the juncture of the foregut and the midgut proceeds to grow cranially and ventrally. This is the hepatic diverticulum, which will develop into the endodermal, or parenchymal, portion of the liver, as well as the epithelium of the biliary apparatus. ■ **Figs. A and B** ■ The hepatic diverticulum grows into the mesenchyme of the septum transversum in which the endodermal cells of the diverticulum form anastomosing hepatic cords. The mesenchyme forms areas of blood islands around the cords. As in early vasculogenesis, some of the mesenchymal cells of the septum transversum develop into endothelial cells around and near the blood islands, and others differentiate along the hematopoietic pathway, making the liver the major site of hematopoiesis during the embryonic and fetal periods. Endothelial cells may further differentiate into hepatic macrophages, known as Kupffer cells. The endothelial-lined channels develop in conjunction with the large vitelline and umbilical blood vessels, which are incorporated into the developing liver to form its intrinsic blood vasculature (see Core Concept 44).

The biliary duct system develops from mesoderm that migrates from the extrahepatic duct system into the parenchyma of the liver. This mesoderm takes up positions around the portal vessels and induces the formation of epithelial ducts from local liver parenchymal cells. Thus, the biliary tract and central vein system is established by the second month of development.

As the liver continues its rapid growth, it maintains its connection to the body wall both dorsally by a mesentery now called the lesser omentum, and ventrally by the falciform ligament. ■ **Fig. C** ■ These structures are derived from septum transversum mesenchyme. Later in development, the lesser omentum contains the gastrohepatic and hepatoduodenal ligaments and has the bile duct as its free edge. The falciform ligament contains the umbilical vein, which is obliterated to become the ligamentum teres after birth.

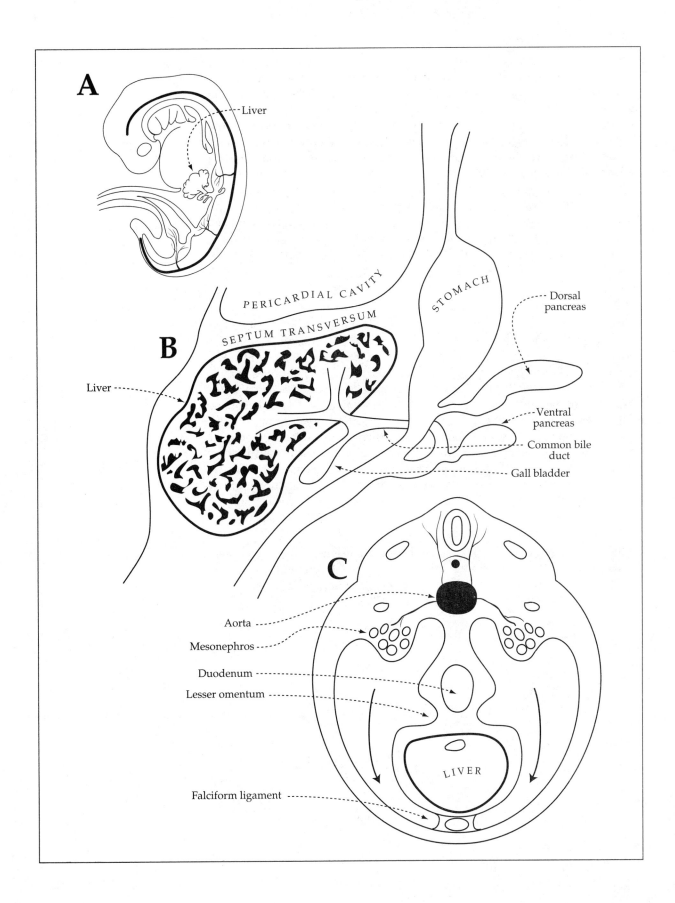

A

Liver

B

PERICARDIAL CAVITY

SEPTUM TRANSVERSUM

STOMACH

Liver

Dorsal pancreas

Ventral pancreas

Common bile duct

Gall bladder

C

Aorta

Mesonephros

Duodenum

Lesser omentum

LIVER

Falciform ligament

52 / Midgut Herniation and Retraction

The rapid expansion of the midgut during the second month of development fills all available space within the abdominal cavity. Further growth of the midgut must take place outside the abdomen until the cavity itself sufficiently expands the following month to accommodate the midgut. This process, referred to as the physiologic herniation of the midgut, takes place from the sixth to the tenth week after fertilization.

Concomitant with midgut herniation is the important phenomenon of midgut rotation. As the midgut initiates herniation, it forms a hairpin loop in the midsagittal plane. The loop is made up of a cephalic limb from the duodenum to its most ventral midpoint, the vitelline duct, and a caudal limb from the vitelline duct to the future transverse colon. The entire midgut loop receives its vascular supply from the superior mesenteric artery, which distributes branches to both limbs from the main artery that forms the axis of the midgut loop. ■ **Fig. A** ■

Within the hernial sac, the midgut rotates 180 degrees counterclockwise. The former cephalic and caudal limbs have now switched positions so that the midgut crosses over itself at the level of the future transverse colon. ■ **Fig. B** ■ At the same time, a slight outpouching of the initial caudal limb of the midgut loop becomes apparent. This cecal bud becomes the focal point of the remainder of midgut rotation, a further 90-degree counterclockwise movement. ■ **Fig. C** ■ This final rotation, bringing the total to 270 degrees, brings the cecum to the upper right quadrant of the midgut (hepatic flexure), from where it descends to the lower right. The appendix subsequently develops as a diverticulum off the cecum. ■ **Fig. D** ■ The mature midgut, still supplied by the superior mesenteric artery and its branches, extends from the distal duodenum to the proximal two-thirds of the transverse colon. The original cephalic limb of the midgut loop forms its juncture with the caudal limb just proximal to the small intestine–ascending colon border.

By the third month of development, the maturing intestines are retracted into the abdomen, and the broad umbilicus is severely reduced. A major subsequent event in GI embryology is the elaboration of the mesentery system and the fixation of the gut tube to the abdominal wall.

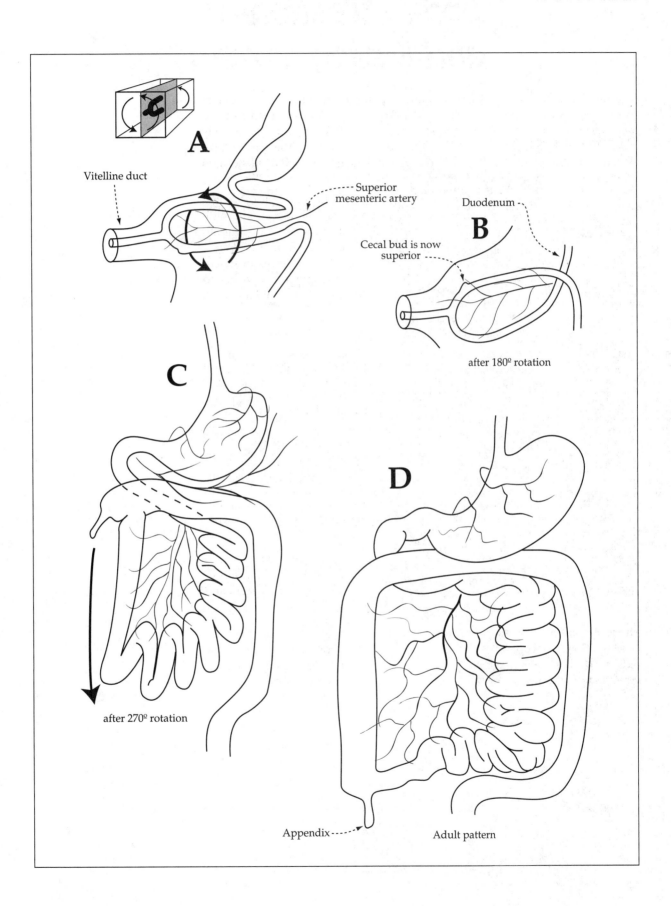

Vitelline duct

Superior mesenteric artery

A

Duodenum

Cecal bud is now superior

B

after 180º rotation

C

after 270º rotation

D

Appendix

Adult pattern

53 / Derivatives of the Dorsal Mesentery and Mesogastrium

The complex growth and rotation of the midgut results in major changes in not only the positioning of the digestive organs but also relationships of the mesenteries, which originally served to suspend the gut in the coelomic cavity. The mesenteries start out as the dorsal and ventral connection of the gut to the body wall along essentially the entire length of the gut. This relatively simple arrangement is basically retained throughout development only for the dorsal mesentery in the midgut. Here the small intestine from the duodenojejunal flexure to the ileocecal junction is attached to the dorsal body wall by the mesentery of the small intestine along an oblique line between these two points. ■ **Fig. A** ■ Similarly, the large intestine retains its dorsal mesentery in regionally identified subdivisions, including the transverse mesocolon, sigmoid mesocolon, and ascending and descending mesocolon. The latter two become retroperitoneal in subsequent development (see Core Concept 54).

The derivatives of the dorsal mesentery in the region of the stomach (mesogastrium) are more complicated. Here the spleen, which develops within the dorsal mesogastrium, may be thought of as dividing this mesentery itself into a dorsal portion, between the spleen and the dorsal body wall, and a ventral portion between the spleen and the stomach. ■ **Fig. B** ■ The dorsal portion differentiates into the splenorenal and phrenicocolic ligaments. The ventral portion gives rise to the very extensive greater omentum, composed of three regional sections: the gastrosplenic ligament, the gastrophrenic ligament, and the huge gastrocolic ligament, which makes up the bulk of the greater omentum. ■ **Fig. C** ■

The mesogastrium is also quite elaborate ventral to the stomach. This mesentery forms the important lesser omentum, which connects the stomach and duodenum to the liver; hence its regional areas are known as the hepatogastric and hepatoduodenal ligaments. See ■ **Fig. C** ■ Additional specially named derivatives of the original ventral mesogastrium attach the liver to the anterior abdominal wall (falciform ligament) and to the diaphragm by way of peritoneal reflections (coronary ligament).

The formation of these various ligaments is driven by the rotation of the stomach (see Core Concept 50) by which the liver swings from the midline to the right. ■ **Fig. B** ■ The space behind the liver and accessible through the epiploic foramen is the lesser sac or bursa.

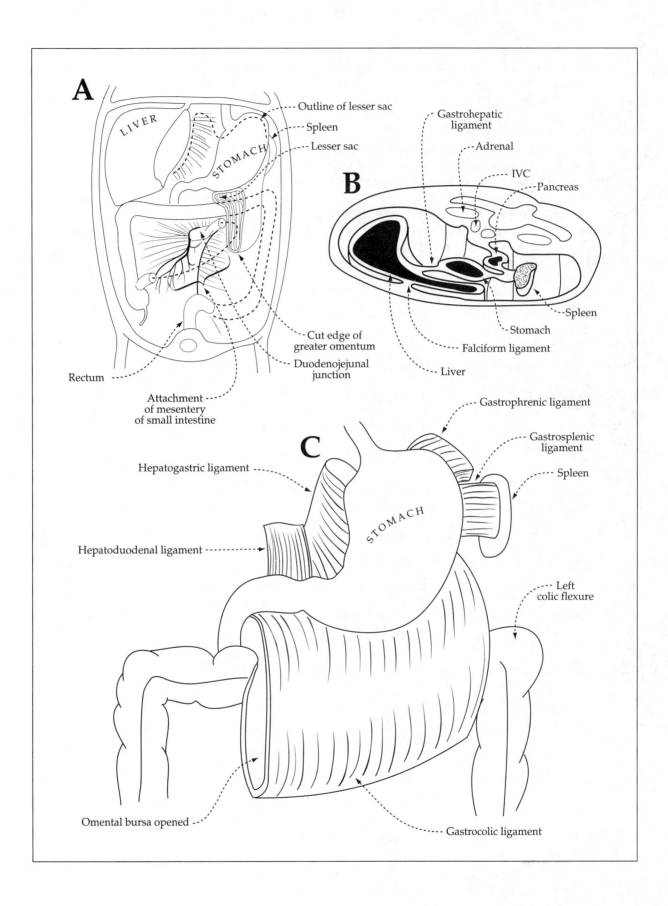

A

LIVER

STOMACH

Outline of lesser sac

Spleen

Lesser sac

B

Gastrohepatic ligament

Adrenal

IVC

Pancreas

Spleen

Stomach

Falciform ligament

Liver

Cut edge of greater omentum

Duodenojejunal junction

Rectum

Attachment of mesentery of small intestine

C

Gastrophrenic ligament

Gastrosplenic ligament

Spleen

Hepatogastric ligament

STOMACH

Hepatoduodenal ligament

Left colic flexure

Omental bursa opened

Gastrocolic ligament

54 / Fixation of the Midgut

On the completion of midgut retraction and the elaboration of the mesenteries, specific portions of the GI system ultimately establish a new relationship to the mesenteries. Whereas initially the entire gut is suspended in the abdominal cavity by a subdivision of the dorsal mesentery, now fusions of specific parts of this mesentery to each other and to the posterior body wall cause these organs attached to the mesentery to become retroperitoneal in position.

Looking at the differentiated GI system ■ **Fig. A** ■ in a midsagittal plane ■ **Fig. B** ■, it is clear that the developing greater omentum is associated with the stomach, duodenum, and pancreas. Both the pancreas and most of the duodenum become retroperitoneally positioned when the portion of the omentum containing these structures fuses with the peritoneum of the posterior abdominal wall. ■ **Fig. C** ■ At the same time, the mesentery supporting the transverse colon fuses with the greater omentum. ■ **Figs. C and D** ■ Finally, the anterior and posterior limbs of the greater omentum fuse to one another. See ■ **Fig. D** ■ This obliterates the potential space of the omentum and forms the caudal extent of the lesser bursa.

Viewing the GI system in transverse section ■ **Fig. E** ■, two additional portions of the gut undergo the same process of fusion to the posterior abdominal wall: the retroperitoneally located ascending and descending colon. In summary, the gut tube establishes a final pattern in which adjacent sections alternate in their position with respect to the abdominal cavity. The duodenum is largely retroperitoneal, the small intestine intraperitoneal. The ascending and descending colon are retroperitoneal, whereas the intervening transverse colon is intraperitoneal. Finally, the sigmoid colon retains its dorsal mesentery and remains in an intraperitoneal position.

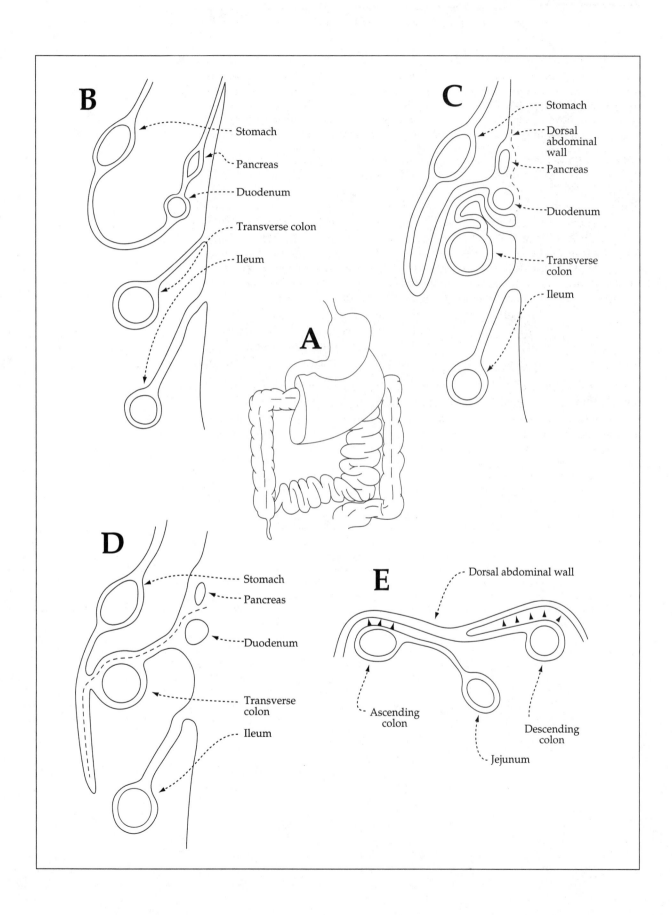

55 / Development of the Urorectal Septum

The development of the hindgut at the end of the first month is intimately tied in with the development of the urogenital system. The terminal portion of the hindgut empties into the proximal expansion of the allantois. The caudal end of this endodermally lined region is called the cloaca. Thus the cloaca is the common distal end of both the early hindgut and the allantois. The ventral aspect of the cloaca is closely apposed to the ectoderm of the body wall, and this double-layered membrane is the proctodeum. ■ **Fig. A** ■

The broad cloaca is divided into a rostral and caudal portion by a wedgelike mass of mesoderm that grows toward the cloaca, the urorectal septum. By the middle of the second month, the rostral part of the cloaca is known as the urogenital sinus and is distinct from the caudal anorectal canal. ■ **Fig. B** ■ On fusion with the cloacal membrane, the urorectal septum forms the perineal body, the former rostral cloacal membrane becomes the urogenital membrane, and the caudal cloacal membrane becomes the anal membrane. ■ **Fig. C** ■ The region in between these two membranes becomes the perineum. The anatomically separated urogenital and GI systems now open out of the ventral body wall when these membranes undergo perforation in subsequent development.

By the end of the second month, the urogenital sinus differentiates into a variety of structures related to both the urinary and the genital system.

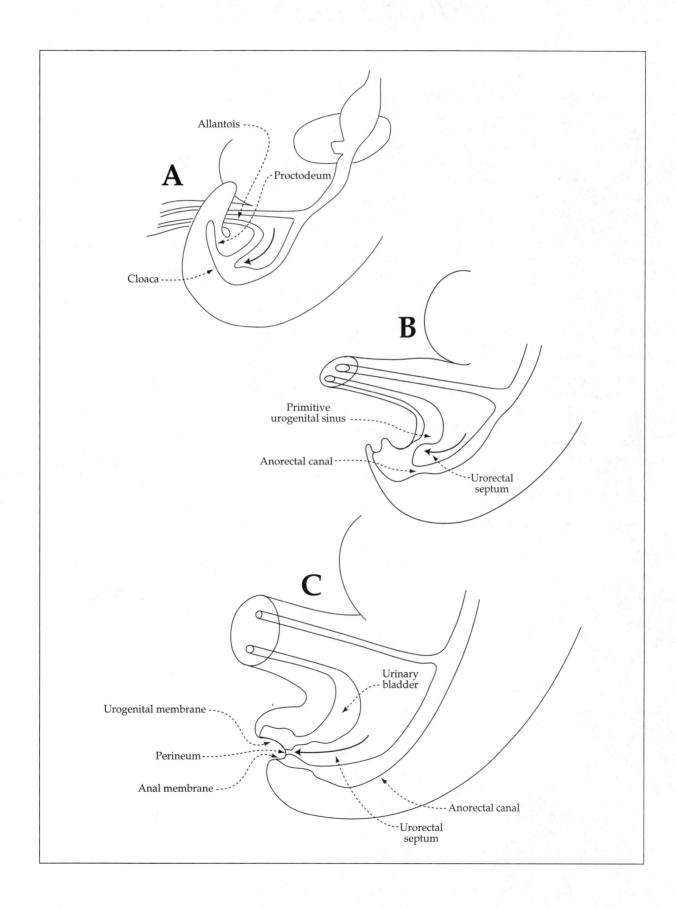

Allantois

A

Proctodeum

Cloaca

B

Primitive
urogenital sinus

Anorectal canal

Urorectal
septum

C

Urinary
bladder

Urogenital membrane

Perineum

Anal membrane

Anorectal canal

Urorectal
septum

56 / Anomalies of the Midgut and Hindgut

The complex and precise developmental program of GI embryology is subject to a host of factors that can go wrong. The small intestine and the duodenum undergo a phase in which their original lumen is obliterated and then recanalized. Failure of recanalization can lead to atresia or stenosis. A section of intestine can also retain remnants of the recanalization process, which leaves septa or cysts in the lumen. ■ **Fig. A** ■

The midgut loop is centered on the vitelline duct, which normally degenerates later in development. Occasionally the proximal portion of the duct is retained as a protrusion of the ileum known as Meckel's diverticulum. Strands of connective tissue from the ileum to the umbilicus can also persist as a vitelline ligament, a vitelline cyst, or even a fistula, providing a patent connection between the bowel and the external abdomen at the level of the ileum and the umbilicus. ■ **Fig. B** ■

Should midgut retraction not occur properly, a herniated sac covered by amnion may protrude through the umbilicus. ■ **Fig. C** ■ This condition, called an omphalocele, requires prompt surgical correction. Finally, a variety of abnormalities in the rotation of the midgut can result in improper positioning of the mature intestinal tract, such as a left colon ■ **Fig. D1** ■ or a partially malrotated (clockwise) gut in which the duodenum is anterior to the colon. ■ **Fig. D2** ■ Such conditions may be largely asymptomatic unless the bowel is actually twisted on itself. Such a condition, known as volvulus, is an extreme emergency because blood supply to that portion of the gut involved in the twisting is compromised.

Anomalies of the hindgut include failure of the anal membrane to rupture (imperforate anus) ■ **Fig. E1** ■ and improper formation or positioning of the urorectal septum. In the latter case, the rectum can open directly into the vagina (rectovaginal fistula) ■ **Fig. E2** ■ or urethra (urorectal fistula). ■ **Fig. E3** ■

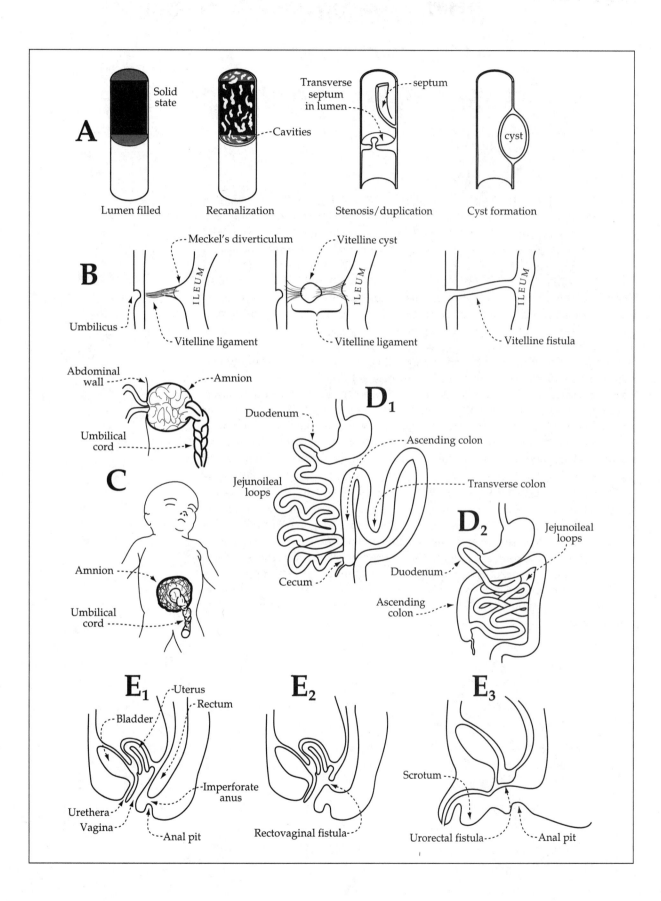

A

Solid state

Lumen filled

Cavities

Recanalization

Transverse septum in lumen — septum

Stenosis/duplication

cyst

Cyst formation

B

Meckel's diverticulum

Vitelline cyst

ILEUM

ILEUM

ILEUM

Umbilicus

Vitelline ligament

Vitelline ligament

Vitelline fistula

Abdominal wall

Amnion

Umbilical cord

C

Amnion

Umbilical cord

D_1

Duodenum

Ascending colon

Transverse colon

Jejunoileal loops

D_2

Jejunoileal loops

Cecum

Duodenum

Ascending colon

E_1

Uterus

Rectum

Bladder

Imperforate anus

Urethera

Vagina

Anal pit

E_2

Rectovaginal fistula

E_3

Scrotum

Urorectal fistula

Anal pit

57 / Development of the Intermediate Mesoderm (Pronephros and Mesonephros)

As discussed in Core Concept 8, the intraembryonic mesoderm gives rise to the intermediate mesoderm, which differentiates into the primitive kidney, known for a very short time as the transient pronephros, and then as the embryonic kidney, or mesonephros. The intermediate mesoderm, like the neighboring paraxial mesoderm, is segmentally arranged. Viewing a cross section through one such segment ■ **Fig. A** ■ reveals that arterial branches from the dorsal aorta migrate laterally to form a tuft of capillaries, known as a glomerulus. ■ **Fig. B** ■ The intermediate mesoderm itself differentiates at the same time by forming a long coiled tubule, the mesonephric tubule. This tubule arises from an epithelial precursor called the nephric vesicle. ■ **Fig. C** ■ One end of this tubule is situated near the inferiolateral portion of the expanding area being taken up by the intermediate mesoderm, which is now called the urogenital ridge. The tubule that connects with each mesonephric tubule and is aligned along the longitudinal axis of the embryo to run continuously through all intermediate mesoderm segments is the mesonephric duct. ■ **Fig. D** ■ The other end of the mesonephric tubule ends in a cup-shaped glomerular cavity in which the glomerulus resides. Blood from the dorsal aorta arrives in the glomerulus via afferent glomerular vessels and is returned to the venous system by the anastomosis of afferent with efferent glomerular vessels. The latter empty into branches of the posterior cardinal and subcardinal system. ■ **Fig. E** ■

When studied in a parasagittal section, it is clear that the most rostral segments of the intermediate mesoderm develop first and then degenerate. ■ **Fig. F** ■ These nonfunctional segments comprise the pronephros. Intermediate mesoderm continues to become segmented in a rostral-to-caudal direction to form the large, functional mesonephros. Even as this prominent structure completes its development during the second month of embryogenesis, the final phase of kidney development, leading to the adult kidney or metanephros, has commenced.

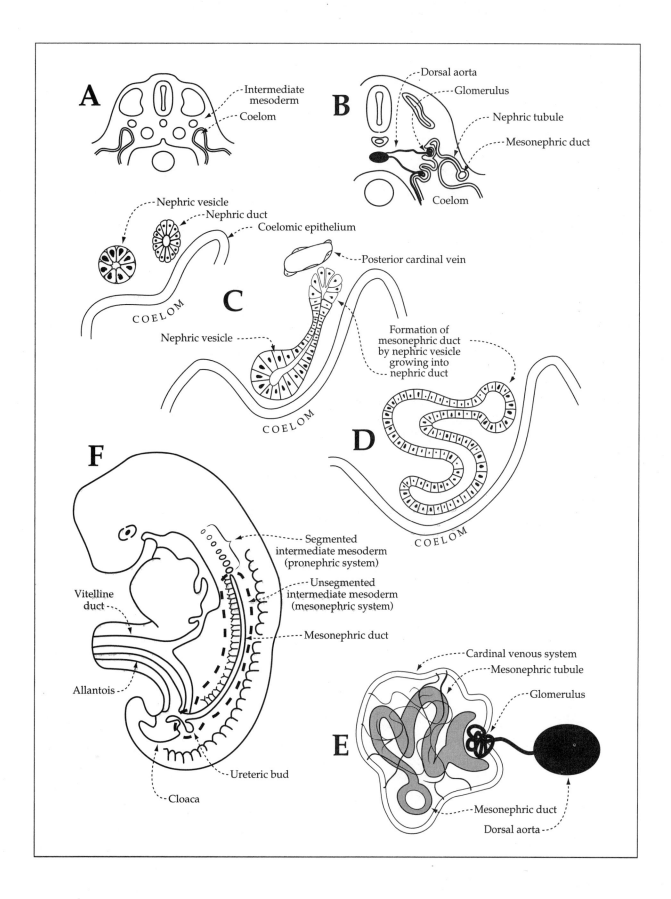

A — Intermediate mesoderm, Coelom

B — Dorsal aorta, Glomerulus, Nephric tubule, Mesonephric duct, Coelom

Nephric vesicle — Nephric duct — Coelomic epithelium — Posterior cardinal vein

C — Nephric vesicle, COELOM

Formation of mesonephric duct by nephric vesicle growing into nephric duct

D — COELOM

F — Segmented intermediate mesoderm (pronephric system), Unsegmented intermediate mesoderm (mesonephric system), Mesonephric duct, Vitelline duct, Allantois, Ureteric bud, Cloaca

E — Cardinal venous system, Mesonephric tubule, Glomerulus, Mesonephric duct, Dorsal aorta

58 Development and Ascent of the Metanephros

The adult kidney, or metanephros, arises as a result of a mesenchymal-epithelial interaction between the metanephric blastema and the ureteric bud. The metanephric blastema consists of mesenchymal tissue, which is loosely organized and inferior to the mesonephros. The epithelial component develops as an outgrowth of the mesonephric duct, known as the ureteric bud, and grows into the metanephric blastema. ■ **Fig. A** ■ As development proceeds, the ureteric bud gradually acquires a separate connection to the posterior wall of the cloaca by moving posteriorly. The ureteric bud may now be called the ureter. ■ **Fig. B** ■

Viewed in longitudinal section at the gross level, the distinction between the two embryologic components of the metanephros remains clear. The ureter divides at the pelvis of the metanephric blastema into calyces. ■ **Fig. C** ■ Their terminal extensions deep within the mesenchyme become the collecting tubules. ■ **Fig. D** ■ Although interactions between the metanephros blastema and ureteric bud start by the second month of development, the process of kidney histodifferentiation occurs over most of the fetal period.

As the ureter lengthens and the embryonic trunk grows, the position of the metanephros gradually changes to take on a more rostral location. ■ **Fig. E** ■ Concurrently, the kidneys rotate about 90 degrees on their longitudinal axes so the ureters are found medial to the kidneys. It is also evident that as the second trimester approaches, the mesonephros is largely degenerating except for its duct system. These surviving ducts will be reutilized to play an important role in the development of the genital system, particularly in the male (see Core Concept 65).

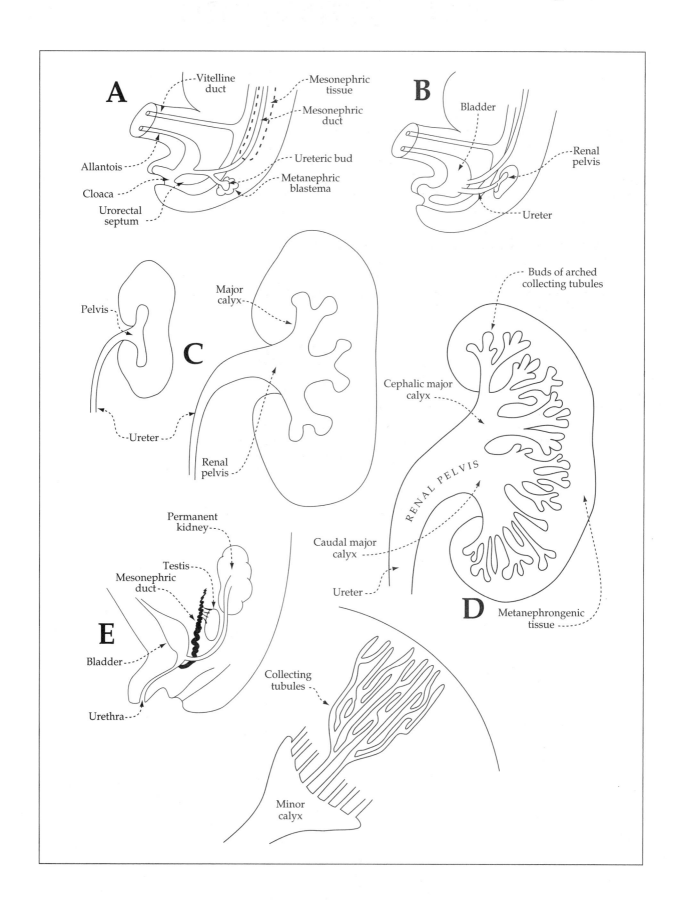

A
Vitelline duct
Mesonephric tissue
Mesonephric duct
Ureteric bud
Metanephric blastema
Allantois
Cloaca
Urorectal septum

B
Bladder
Renal pelvis
Ureter

C
Pelvis
Major calyx
Ureter
Renal pelvis

D
Buds of arched collecting tubules
Cephalic major calyx
RENAL PELVIS
Caudal major calyx
Ureter
Metanephrongenic tissue

E
Permanent kidney
Testis
Mesonephric duct
Bladder
Urethra
Collecting tubules
Minor calyx

59 / Functional Histology of the Metanephros

At the junction of the collecting tubules and the metanephric blastema, the nephron, the basic functional unit of the kidney, begins to differentiate. In many respects, this process resembles the differentiation of the mesonephros (see Core Concept 57). The first indication of this process is the formation of small epithelial vesicles, known as renal vesicles, which are induced in the mesenchyme by the proximal ends of the branches of the ureteric bud, known as collecting tubules. ■ **Fig. A** ■ Thus, certain cells of the metanephric blastema undergo mesenchymal-epithelial transformation. The renal vesicles begin to elongate to form renal tubules, or nephrons. ■ **Fig. B** ■ As elongation proceeds, the proximal end of the nephron curves back on itself to form a cuplike pocket. Within this pocket, vasculogenesis takes place from other cells of the metanephric blastema. Finally, the distal end of the nephron fuses to and becomes continuous with the proximal end of the collecting tubule from which the nephron was originally induced.

At this point the nephron has lengthened to such an extent that regional differences in its position and structure may be discerned. ■ **Fig. C** ■ The portion adjacent to the collecting tubule becomes the distal convoluted tubule, the intermediate part greatly elongates to form the loop of Henle, and the proximal-most segment of the renal tubule differentiates into the proximal convoluted tubule. At the end of the proximal convoluted tubule, vascularization of the double-walled cup itself has become quite extensive and now is termed the glomerulus. ■ **Fig. D** ■ The double-walled cup itself, which envelops the glomerulus, becomes Bowman's capsule. Cells of this capsule undergo further differentiation so that the inner wall cells become specialized for ultrafiltration. These are known as podocytes. ■ **Fig. E** ■

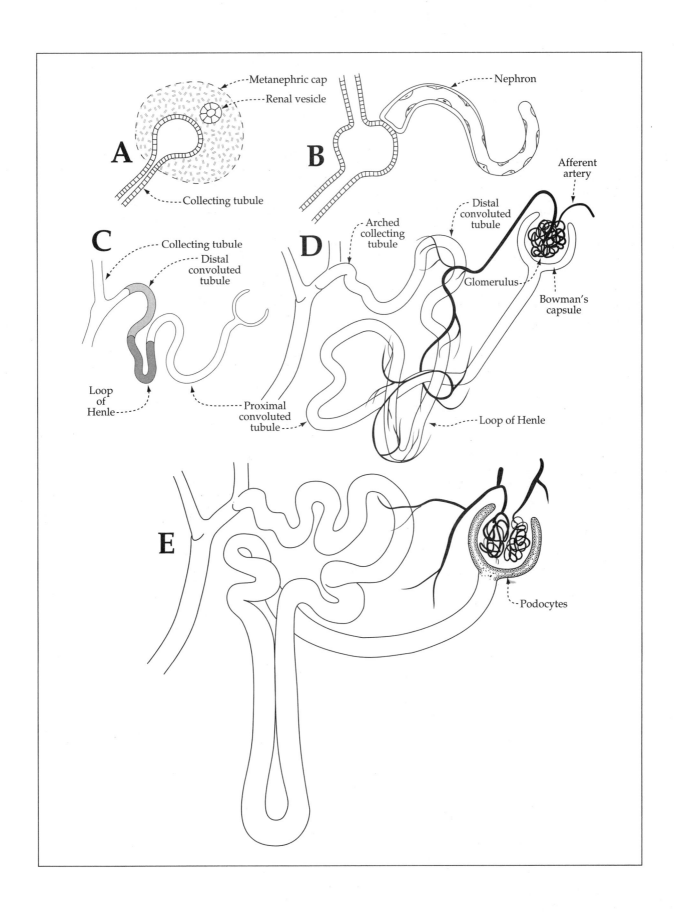

A — Metanephric cap, Renal vesicle, Collecting tubule

B — Nephron

C — Collecting tubule, Distal convoluted tubule, Loop of Henle, Proximal convoluted tubule

D — Arched collecting tubule, Distal convoluted tubule, Afferent artery, Glomerulus, Bowman's capsule, Loop of Henle

E — Podocytes

60 / Development of the Bladder and Urethra

The urogenital sinus, a derivative of the primitive cloaca (see Core Concept 55), differentiates into specific regional zones in the second month of development. Since the sinus is continuous rostrally with the allantois, the extraembryonic membrane that forms as a diverticulum of the early hindgut, the entire structure is elongated and crescent shaped. ■ **Fig. A** ■ The rostral part of the urogenital sinus expands to become the urinary bladder. Its most rostral tip terminates at the umbilicus as a fibrous cord known as the urachus. The caudal-most portion of the urogenital sinus is the genital zone, which will differentiate into the penile urethra in the male. ■ **Fig. B** ■ The middle part of the urogenital sinus, between the future bladder and the genital region, is the pelvic zone of the urogenital sinus. The lower prostatic and membranous urethra form from the pelvic portion of the urogenital sinus. In the male, the rostral portion of the urogenital sinus also differentiates into the endodermal lining of the prostatic urethra. Later budding of the epithelium off the cranial urethra will invade surrounding mesenchyme to become the prostate glands. Finally, the penile urethra develops by canalization of an ectoderm core. In the female, the entire urethra is derived from the rostral portion of the urogenital sinus, which also gives rise to the bladder. ■ **Fig. C** ■

The posterior aspect of the bladder itself receives two sets of ducts early in development. During the second month, the ureters move more laterally and cranially relative to the mesonephric ducts. The region of the bladder bordered by the openings of the ureters and the mesonephric ducts is originally covered by mesoderm of the ducts and has a distinctive triangular appearance known as the trigone. ▨ **Figs. D and E** ■ In subsequent development the mesonephric ducts in the female will degenerate, whereas in the male they will further differentiate into the vas deferens (see Core Concepts 64 and 65).

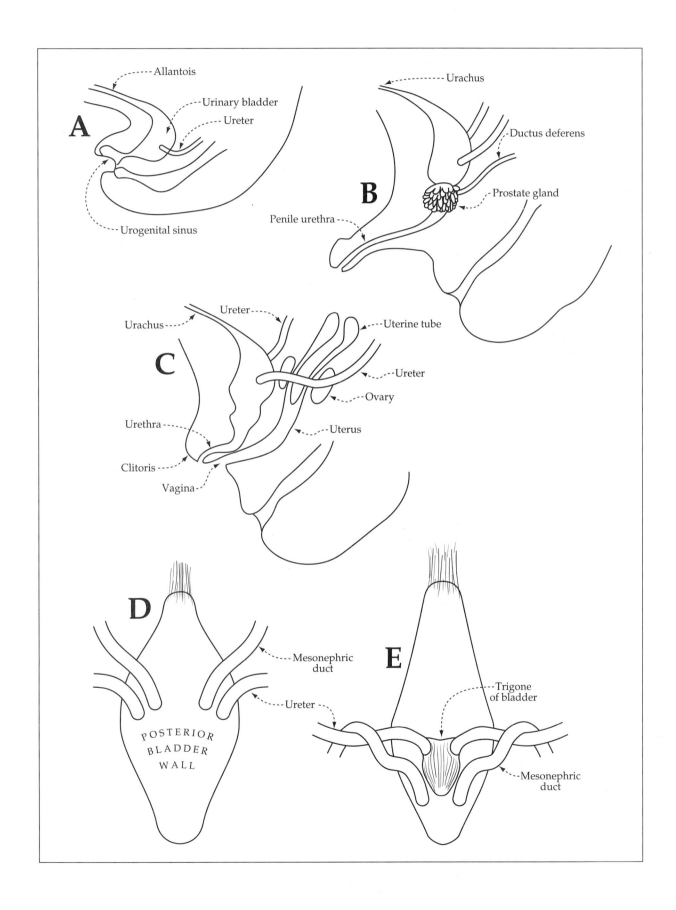

61 / Anomalies of Urinary System Development

The wide array of congenital anomalies of the urinary system may be grouped into several categories. The broadest group contains the anomalies of size and/or number of the kidneys and ureters. Examples of such malformations include the total absence of the kidney (unilateral or bilateral renal agenesis), extrarenal tissue (supernumerary kidney), and incomplete development of the kidney (renal hypoplasia). ■ **Fig. A** ■ The basis of such anomalies most likely stems from the early interaction between the ureteric bud and metanephric blastema. A failure of the two to interact may lead to agenesis, incomplete interaction to hypoplasia, and dispersed, rather than focal, interaction to an ectopic or supernumerary organ. Similar considerations hold for the ureter. An absent, additional, or branched ureter may be embryologically traced to an absent, branched, or duplicated ureteric bud in the second month of development. ■ **Fig. B** ■

Anomalies in the migration and/or rotation of the kidneys ■ **Fig. C** ■ may result in a pelvic kidney or an ectopic pelvic kidney ipsilateral to a normal kidney. The latter condition is known as crossed ectopia. During their migration to the abdomen, the inferior poles of the kidneys may contact one another and fuse to produce a horseshoe kidney. Typically, such a kidney migrates to the level of the inferior mesenteric artery, where it is blocked from further ascent.

Congenital polycystic kidney is a disease thought to arise from the failure of the two embryologic components of the metanephros, the collecting tubules and the nephron, to join properly. A large number of fluid-filled cysts make up the major part of the kidney.

Congenital anomalies of the bladder include the persistence of remnants of the urachus at the rostral end of the bladder. ■ **Fig. D** ■ Such anomalies may be limited to a urachal sinus or a blind urachal cyst. In other instances, a fistula between the bladder and the umbilicus, resulting in a continuity of bladder contents with the umbilicus, may persist.

In rare instances, the posterior bladder wall may protrude through the abdomen due to improper development of the abdominal wall. This condition, known as exstrophy of the bladder ■ **Fig. E** ■, is often associated with major defects in the genital system, particularly in the male.

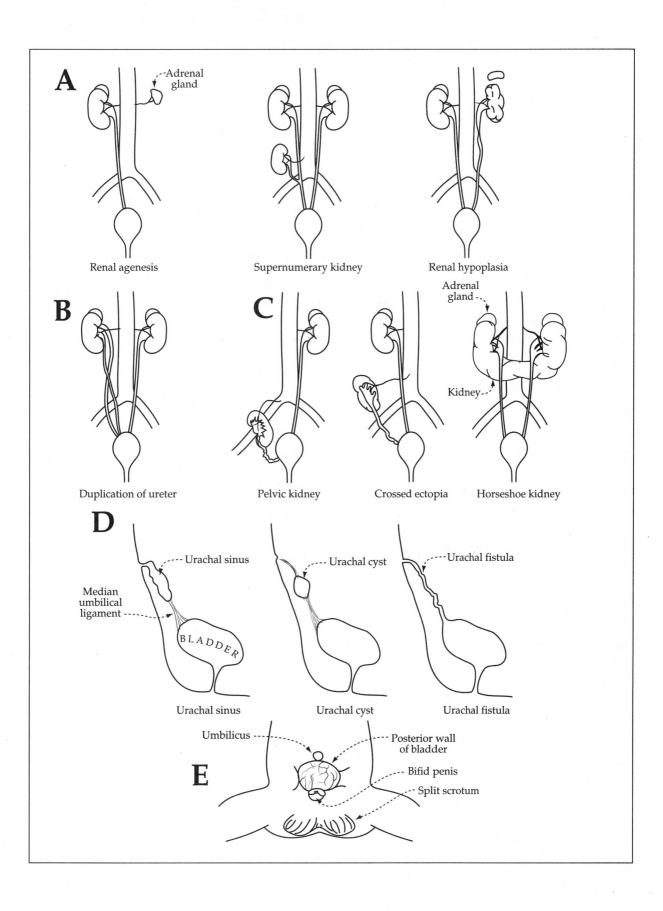

A

Renal agenesis
Adrenal gland

Supernumerary kidney

Renal hypoplasia

B

Duplication of ureter

C

Pelvic kidney

Crossed ectopia

Horseshoe kidney
Adrenal gland
Kidney

D

Urachal sinus
Median umbilical ligament
BLADDER

Urachal sinus

Urachal cyst

Urachal cyst

Urachal fistula

Urachal fistula

E

Umbilicus
Posterior wall of bladder
Bifid penis
Split scrotum

62 / Early Development of the Genital System: Gonadal Development

The first indications of the development of the genital system occur early in the second month postfertilization. Individual primordial germ cells migrate from their site of origin in the endoderm of the yolk sac and allantois to the germinal ridge, an area along the ventral body wall just medial to the large mesonephros. ■ **Fig. A** ■ Over the next few weeks the primordial germ cells, surrounding mesenchyme, and underlying coelomic epithelium interact to produce a morphologically differentiated gonad.

This process is initiated by the proliferation of the coelomic epithelium inward toward the mesenchyme to form columnlike projections, the primary sex cords. ■ **Fig. B** ■ These cords establish a close association with the germ cells they encounter. At about the sixth week, the sex cords are still continuous with the coelomic epithelium and form extensive anastomoses with one another. ■ **Fig. C** ■ This represents the indifferent stage of gonad development because the sex of the gonad cannot yet be established morphologically. Soon after, the program for sex differentiation, determined genetically at fertilization through the sex chromosome, will progress to the point where gonadal sex may be anatomically established.

In the male, the sex cords reach the medulla of the gonad by further proliferation. In the female, these cords degenerate, and a new wave of sex cord proliferation, the secondary sex cords, begins. These sex cords, however, reach only the outer, or cortical, regions of the gonad, where they tend to break down, and the cells of the cords surround primary germ cells. Hence, the sex cords tend to be present throughout the entire testis, and particularly in the medullary areas, but are restricted to the cortex in the ovary. ■ **Fig. D** ■

At the gross level, the gonad separates from the medial aspect of the mesonephros by the ingrowth of deep grooves. See ■ **Fig. D** ■. These ultimately form the gonadal mesentery (mesorchium or mesovarium).

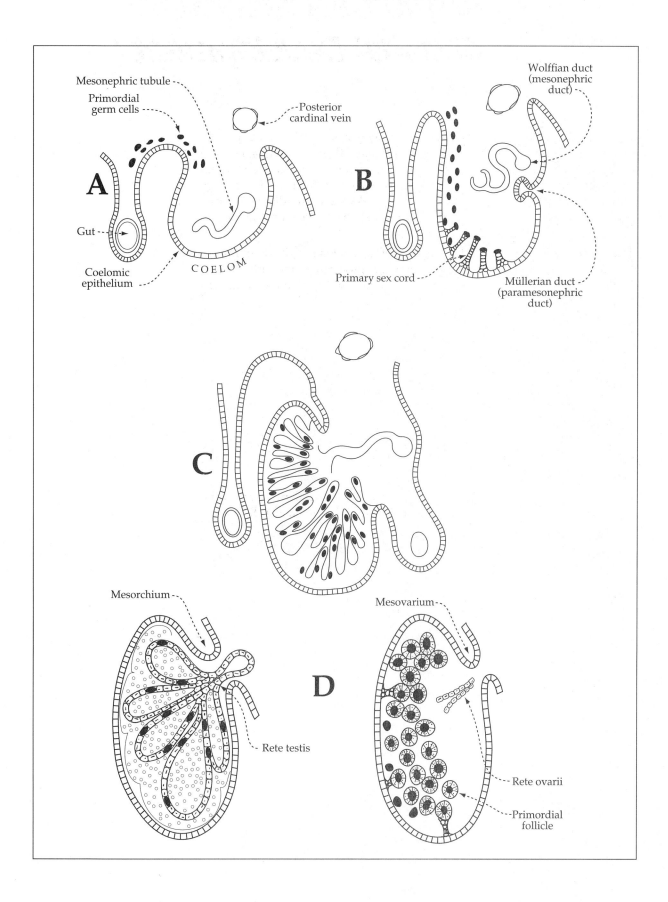

A — Mesonephric tubule · · Primordial germ cells · · · Posterior cardinal vein · Gut · · Coelomic epithelium · · COELOM

B — Wolffian duct (mesonephric duct) · · Primary sex cord · · Müllerian duct (paramesonephric duct)

C

D — Mesorchium · · Mesovarium · · Rete testis · Rete ovarii · Primordial follicle

63 Male and Female Gonadal Histodifferentiation and Early Development of the Genital System

As the primary sex cords of the testes continue to develop, their proximal ends begin to form an interconnected complex known as the rete testis. At the same time, a prominent connective tissue capsule envelops the testis. This tunica albuginea sends shelflike projections inward toward the rete testis and partitions the testis into a number of compartments. ■ **Fig. A** ■ The major portion of the male sex cords thus differentiates into the coiled seminiferous tubules. The remainder contribute to the tubuli recti and rete testis. In the mature testis, spermatogonia arise from the primordial germ cells and Sertoli cells from the germinal epithelium, which has grown inward to form the sex cords. The steroid-producing Leydig cells differentiate from the interstitial mesenchyme, the third component of the developing gonad. ■ **Fig. B** ■

The development of the ovary is characterized by the differentiation of the secondary sex cords into follicle cells, which envelop individual oogonia. ■ **Fig. C** ■ The oogonia proliferate during fetal development and enter a resting state before birth. ■ **Fig. D** ■ A tunica albuginea, thinner than that found in the testes, surrounds the ovary.

In the indifferent stage of gonad development, the mesonephros develops two separate, parallel duct systems (also see Core Concept 62). One of these, the original mesonephric (Wolffian) duct, runs along the lateral side of the gonad. The other, the paramesonephric (Müllerian) duct, develops just lateral and inferior to the mesonephric duct. See ■ **Figs. A and C** ■ Under the influence of sex-specific humoral factors, only the mesonephric duct system is retained in the male and the paramesonephric system in the female. The detailed embryologic fate of those two duct systems will be described in Core Concepts 64 and 65.

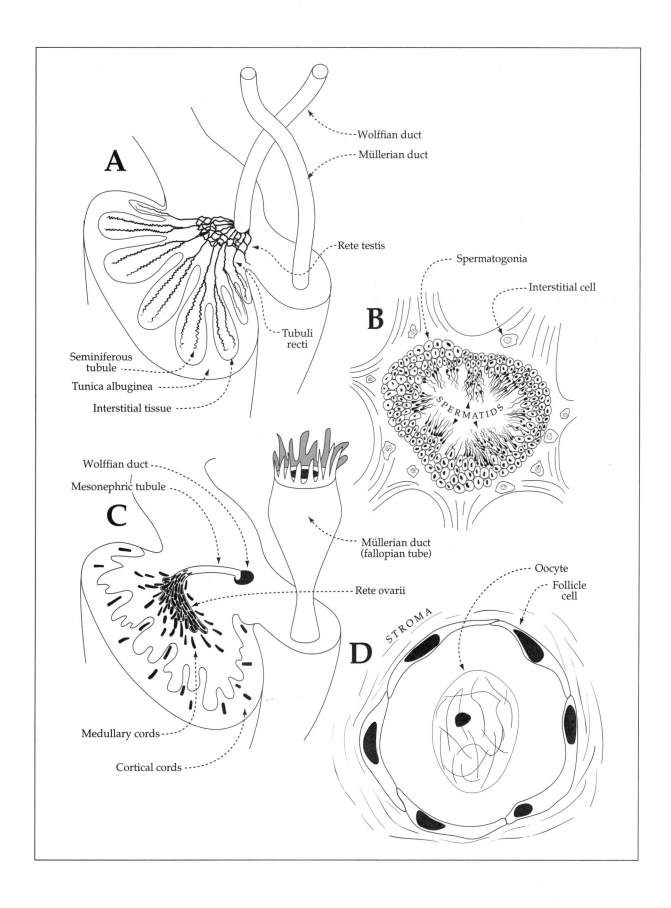

64 / Later Female Genital Duct Development

The paramesonephric ducts, which run lateral to the mesonephric ducts at the midlevel of the gonad, cross the mesonephric ducts anteriorly and fuse with one another near their inferior ends. ■ **Fig. A1** ■ This swinging of the paramesonephric ducts toward the midline ■ **Fig. A2** ■ results in the transverse pelvic fold, or broad ligament, which acts to suspend the fused paramesonephric ducts and, more laterally, the ovaries by way of the mesovarium. ■ **Fig. A3** ■

The paramesonephric ducts end distally at the genital tubercle near the posterior end of the urogenital sinus. The fused portion of the ducts expands to form the primitive uterus and the proximal, unfused portion of the ducts differentiates into the uterine, or Fallopian, tubes. ■ **Fig. B** ■ The uterine tubes terminate in the fimbria, which are closely associated with the ovaries.

The junction of the uterus and the genital tubercle lengthens as the cells of the urogenital sinus proliferate to form the tissue of the embryonic vagina. ■ **Fig. C1** ■ This solid mass begins to canalize by the third month of gestation and eventually differentiates into the proximal portion of the vagina. ■ **Fig. C2** ■ The vagina distal to the hymen is derived from the remainder of the urogenital sinus and forms the vestibule. Lateral diverticula of the urogenital sinus will differentiate into Bartholin's glands during midgestation. ■ **Fig. C3** ■

In the female reproductive system at term ■ **Fig. D** ■, remnants of the mesonephric duct include the epoöphoron, from the mesonephric tubules at the level of the ovary, and the paroöphoron, located farther distally along the former mesonephric duct. In addition, remnants of this duct along the lateral border of the uterus may form cystic swellings, known as Gartner's duct cysts. The inferior ligament of the ovary becomes the round ligament, which terminates at the genital swellings, as does the male gubernaculum.

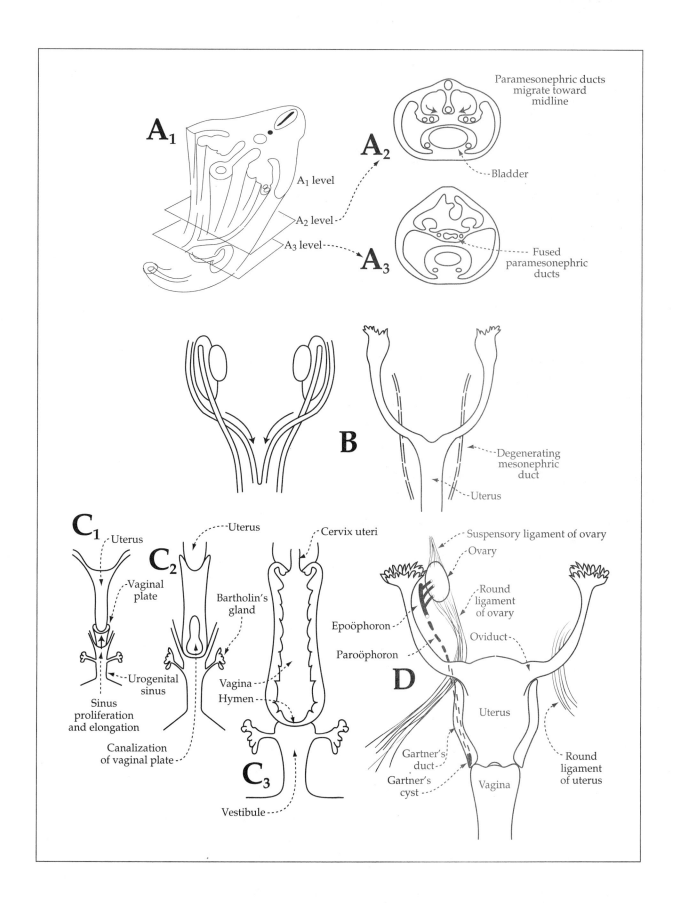

A_1

A_2

Paramesonephric ducts
migrate toward
midline

Bladder

A_3

A_1 level

A_2 level

A_3 level

Fused
paramesonephric
ducts

B

Degenerating
mesonephric
duct

Uterus

C_1 Uterus

C_2 Uterus

Cervix uteri

Suspensory ligament of ovary

Ovary

Vaginal
plate

Bartholin's
gland

Round
ligament
of ovary

Epoöphoron

Oviduct

Paroöphoron

Urogenital
sinus

Vagina

Hymen

D

Uterus

Sinus
proliferation
and elongation

Canalization
of vaginal plate

C_3

Gartner's
duct

Gartner's
cyst

Round
ligament
of uterus

Vagina

Vestibule

65 / Later Male Genital Duct Development

In the male, the surviving mesonephric ducts assume an entirely different function from their original role as a conduit for the embryonic kidney. During the third month of development, the mesonephric, or Wolffian, ducts and a few associated mesonephric tubules located at the level of the developing testes are taken over as the duct system of the male reproductive tract. ■ **Fig. A** ■ The mesonephric duct differentiates into the epididymis and vas deferens and its rostral, nonfunctional end becomes the appendix epididymis. The surviving mesonephric tubules are converted into the vas efferentes, and the remnants of the degenerating tubules inferior to the efferent ductules become the paradidymis. ■ **Fig. B** ■ Although the paramesonephric, or müllerian, ducts degenerate in the male, they usually leave behind two remnants, one at either end of the duct. At its superior end, the appendix testis forms a slight hillock on the superior pole of the testis, and at its inferior end, the two fused paramesonephric ducts form a blind pouch known as the prostatic utricle. See ■ **Fig. B** ■

During the second trimester, numerous glands develop as outgrowths of the male genital tract. ■ **Fig. C** ■ Near the distal ends of the vas deferens, the seminal vesicles emerge. Inferior to this point, the vas deferens forms the ejaculatory duct. The prostatic urethra, derived from the urogenital sinus (Core Concept 60), elaborates the glands of the prostate. Further distally, two additional sets of glands emerge from the penile urethra: the bulbourethral glands and the more distal urethral glands.

The final major event in male genital duct development occurs late in fetal life with the descent of the testis. ■ **Fig. D** ■ Differential growth of the trunk coupled with the active participation of the gubernaculum, a ligamentlike remnant of the inferior mesonephros, results in the migration of the testes through the abdominal wall along the developing inguinal canal to its final position in the genital swelling. See Core Concept 66.

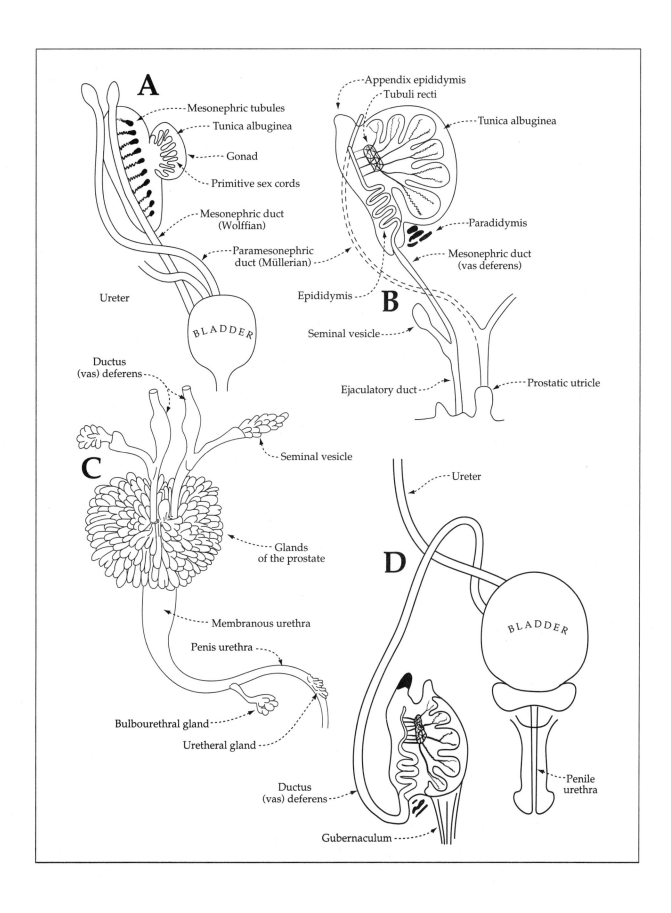

A
- Mesonephric tubules
- Tunica albuginea
- Gonad
- Primitive sex cords
- Mesonephric duct (Wolffian)
- Paramesonephric duct (Müllerian)

Ureter

BLADDER

B
- Appendix epididymis
- Tubuli recti
- Tunica albuginea
- Paradidymis
- Mesonephric duct (vas deferens)
- Epididymis
- Seminal vesicle
- Ejaculatory duct
- Prostatic utricle

C
- Ductus (vas) deferens
- Seminal vesicle
- Glands of the prostate
- Membranous urethra
- Penis urethra
- Bulbourethral gland
- Uretheral gland

D
- Ureter
- BLADDER
- Penile urethra
- Ductus (vas) deferens
- Gubernaculum

66 / Development of the External Genitalia

The external genitalia develop from the third to the seventh week, passing through an indifferent stage in which both the male and female appear morphologically identical. This stage begins with the proliferation of mesenchyme into the cloacal region, resulting in an elevation of this area when viewed externally. ■ **Fig. A** ■ This cloacal fold is demarcated along the lateral border of the elongated cloacal membrane by folds of epithelium-covered mesenchyme called the urogenital folds. ■ **Fig. B** ■ At the rostral end of the cloaca the urogenital folds meet to form a midline genital tubercle. Concurrently, the caudal end of the genital folds join to form the perineal body, which externally separates the urogenital membrane from the anal membrane. The genital folds continue posteriorly as the anal fold to envelop the anal membrane. ■ **Fig. C** ■

By the end of the second month of development, sexual dimorphism with respect to the external genitalia is obvious. In the female, the genital tubercle develops into the glans clitoridis. The urogenital membrane ruptures to form the urethral groove ■ **Fig. D** ■, the genital folds become the labia minora, and the genital swelling the labia majora. ■ **Fig. E** ■ By the third month, vaginal development has proceeded to a point where the vestibule, derived from the urogenital sinus, has attained continuity with the vaginal plate to form the hymen (see Core Concept 65).

In the male, the rupture of the urogenital membrane to form the urethral groove is followed by the thickening of the epithelium lining the groove. This urethral plate then folds on itself in the ventral midline to produce the penile urethra. ■ **Fig. F** ■ The genital swellings expand during the fusion of the urethral folds in the male and develop into the scrotum. ■ **Fig. G** ■ As the glans penis continues to enlarge and the penile urethra lengthens, the glans undergoes a cavitation phase in which the solid glandular plate breaks down to form the navicular fossa and the preputial plate, running circumferentially around the glans, breaks down to form the prepuce. ■ **Fig. H** ■ The meeting of the penile urethra and the hollowed-out glandular plate completes the continuity of the urogenital tract in the male.

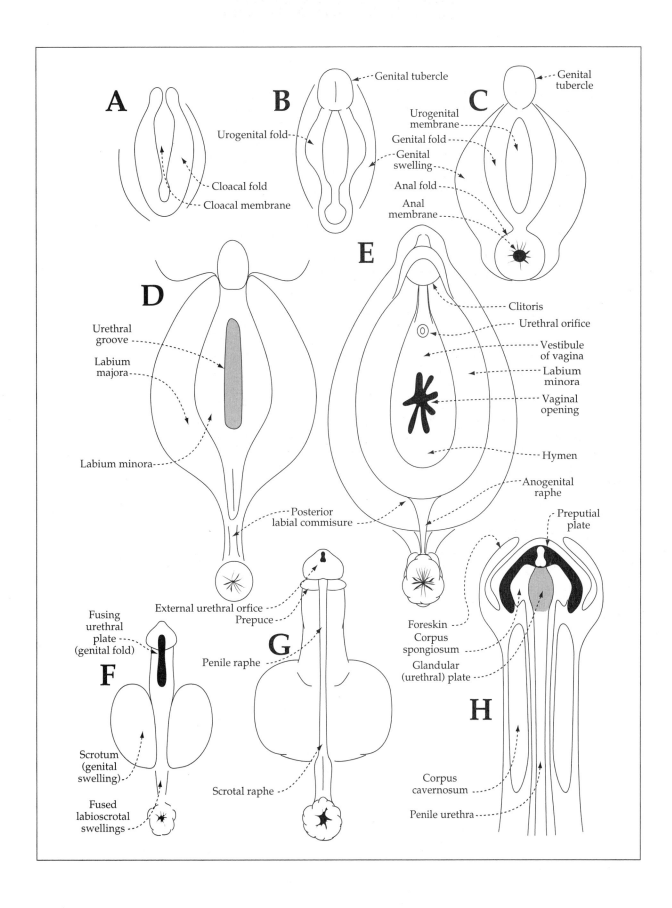

A

B — Genital tubercle

Urogenital fold

C — Genital tubercle

Urogenital membrane
Genital fold
Genital swelling
Anal fold
Anal membrane

Cloacal fold
Cloacal membrane

D

Urethral groove
Labium majora
Labium minora

E — Clitoris
— Urethral orifice
— Vestibule of vagina
— Labium minora
— Vaginal opening
— Hymen
— Anogenital raphe

Posterior labial commisure

F

Fusing urethral plate (genital fold)

External urethral orifice
Prepuce

Penile raphe

G

Scrotum (genital swelling)

Fused labioscrotal swellings

Scrotal raphe

H — Preputial plate

Foreskin
Corpus spongiosum
Glandular (urethral) plate

Corpus cavernosum

Penile urethra

67 / Anomalies of Genital System Development

Congenital malformations of the female internal genitalia most commonly arise from the incomplete or nonsymmetrical fusion of the paramesonephric ducts or improper development of the urogenital sinus. For example, a complete or partial midline septum in the uterus may result from failure of the paramesonephric ducts to fuse fully after contacting one another. ■ **Fig. A1** ■ Failure of the ducts ever to make contact may cause a double uterus to form. ■ **Fig. A2** ■ Paired vaginas may accompany this anomaly, suggesting that each uterine horn may be sufficient to induce the development of a vaginal plate. Failure of one paramesonephric duct to form may result in a unicornate uterus. ■ **Fig. A3** ■ Malformations of the genital tubercle or vaginal plate may manifest themselves in cervical atresia ■ **Fig. A4** ■, and vaginal atresia may be due to abnormal development of the sinovaginal bulb. ■ **Fig. A5** ■

Although congenital absence or malformation of the mesonephric ducts in males is known to occur, most anomalies of the male genital system are associated with the external genitalia. Hypospadias is a result of incomplete fusion of the penile urethra along the ventrum of the penis. Urethral openings may appear abnormally at any point along the penile urethra and may be quite extensive ■ **Fig. B1** ■ or restricted ■ **Fig. B2** ■. Epispadias is thought to be due to the improper positioning of the genital tubercle early in development. When the glans develops more inferiorly than normal, the opening of the urethra may occur on the dorsum of the penis. ■ **Fig. C1** ■ Again, like hypospadias, epispadias may leave the entire penile urethra exposed, in this case, along the dorsal aspect. ■ **Fig. C2** ■ This condition is often associated with exstrophy of the bladder, although the embryologic mechanism underlying these malfunctions appears to be separate.

The external genitalia of either genetic males or females may develop ambiguously. This condition, known as pseudohermaphrodism, is characterized by varying degrees of labial fusion and clitoromegaly in genetic females ■ **Fig. D** ■ and hypoplasia of the penis in males.

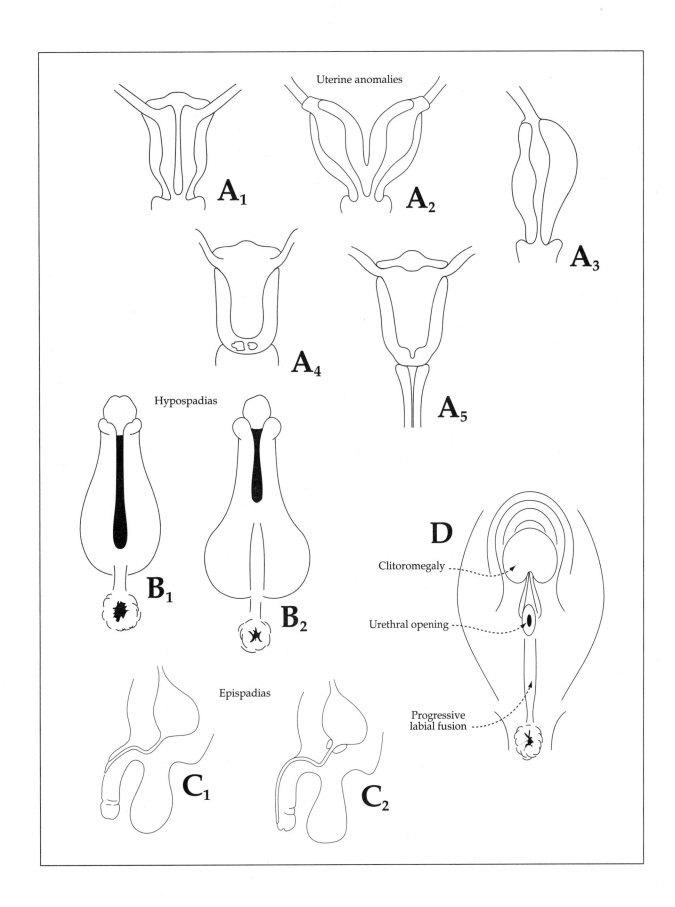

Uterine anomalies

A₁ A₂ A₃ A₄ A₅

Hypospadias

B₁ B₂

Epispadias

C₁ C₂

D

Clitoromegaly

Urethral opening

Progressive labial fusion

68 / *Neural Tube Closure*

During the third week of development when the process of gastrulation is a major embryologic event, another important event is taking place on the dorsal surface of the embryo (also see Core Concept 7). The ectoderm becomes thickened and takes on an hourglass appearance along the axis of the embryo. ■ **Fig. A** ■ The lateral edges of this thickened ectoderm, known as neuroectoderm, grow toward each other. As the neuroectoderm in the midline sinks into the dorsal surface of the embryo, a furrow forms and then a deep groove, and finally a tube. ■ **Fig. B** ■ The neural tube closes by a contraction of the apical domain of the neuroepithelial cells, in effect resembling the closing of a purse-string. ■ **Fig. C** ■ The formation of the neural tube occurs progressively by beginning near the middle of the embryo during the fourth week of development and proceeding in both a rostral and caudal direction. The final parts of the neural tube to close are on the extreme cranial and caudal ends of the embryo, known as the anterior and posterior neuropore, respectively. Failure of the neuropores, or any other part of the neural tube, to close has important implications and may result in a variety of serious congenital anomalies known as neural tube defects (see Core Concept 73).

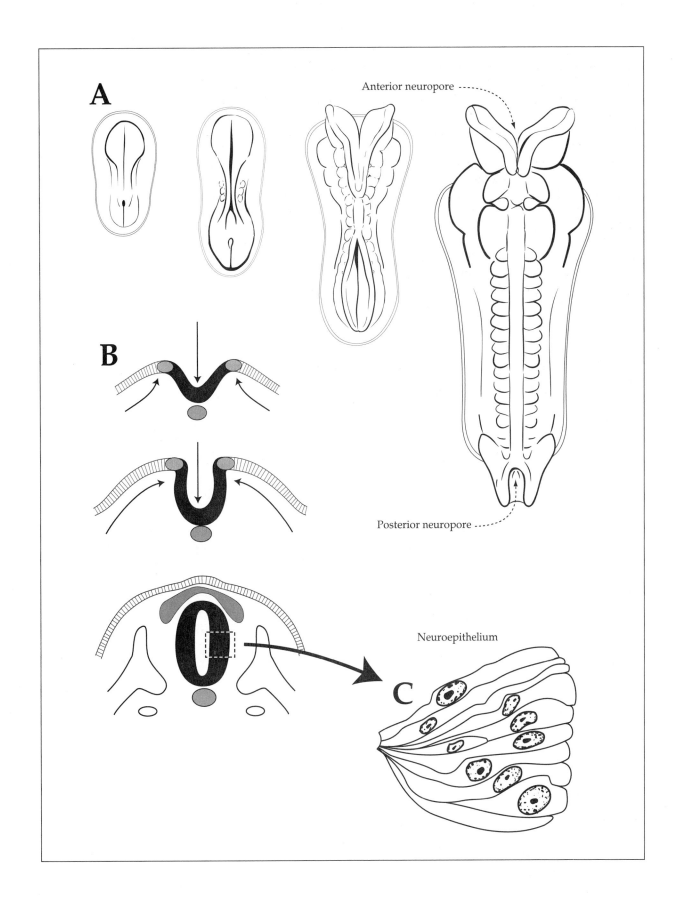

A

Anterior neuropore

B

Posterior neuropore

Neuroepithelium

C

69 / Flexure and Expansion of the Neural Tube

The rostral end of the neural tube, the most prominent part of the developing nervous system from its first appearance as neural ectoderm, develops a series of regional expansions during the fifth week of development. The rostral-most expansion is the forebrain, or prosencephalon, followed by the midbrain, or mesencephalon, and finally the hindbrain, or rhombencephalon. ■ **Fig. A** ■ Later these three primary vesicles expand into five secondary vesicles. ■ **Fig. B** ■ The forebrain gives rise to the telencephalon and diencephalon. The former develops into the massive cerebral hemispheres and the latter into the thalamic complex. The midbrain remains relatively small and retains its name. The hindbrain, like the forebrain, also divides into two secondary vesicles: the metencephalon, which largely becomes the cerebellum and pons, and the myelencephalon, which develops into the medulla oblongata. Soon after the establishment of the secondary vesicles, the rostral end of the embryo undergoes marked flexures in two positions. The cerebral flexure takes place between the midbrain and hindbrain, and the cervical flexure creates a right-angle bend in the embryo at the hindbrain to spinal cord level.

The entire neural tube retains its central canal in the developing brain; however, important modifications of the simple canal develop in this region. ■ **Fig. C** ■ Viewing the embryo from a dorsal projection, this is especially apparent in the telencephalon, where expansive lateral extensions of the central canal develop. These bilaterally symmetrical structures are known as the first and second, or lateral, ventricles. They converge in the anterior part of the diencephalon to form the third ventricle, form the narrow aqueduct of Sylvius through the midbrain, and finally expand again in the dorsal hindbrain to form the fourth ventricle. The entire ventricular system and central canal are filled with cerebrospinal fluid, which is produced by the choroid plexus, specialized cells lining specific portions of the ventricles.

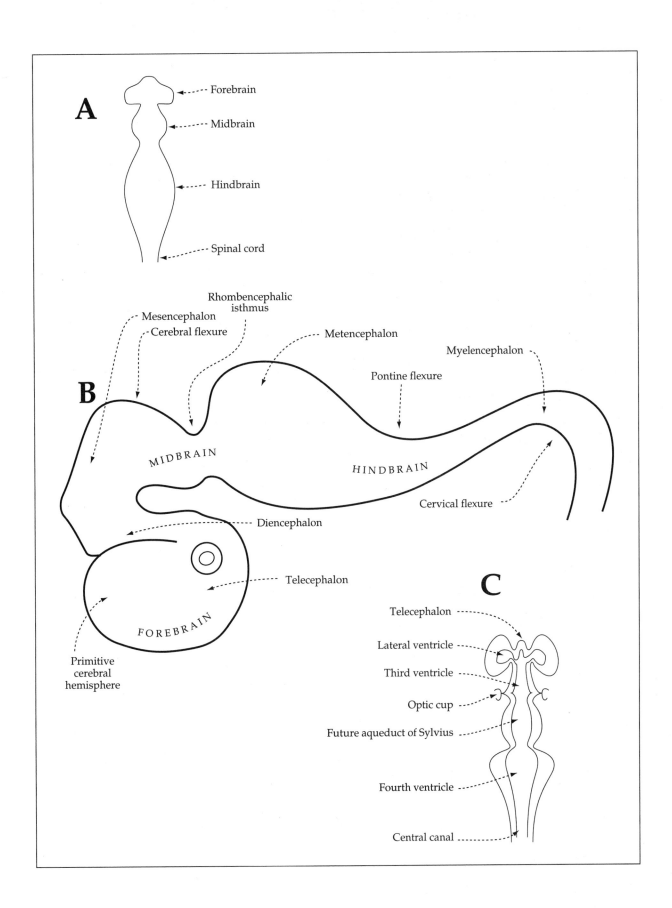

A

- Forebrain
- Midbrain
- Hindbrain
- Spinal cord

B

Rhombencephalic isthmus

Mesencephalon

Cerebral flexure

Metencephalon

Myelencephalon

Pontine flexure

MIDBRAIN

HINDBRAIN

Cervical flexure

Diencephalon

Telecephalon

FOREBRAIN

Primitive cerebral hemisphere

C

- Telecephalon
- Lateral ventricle
- Third ventricle
- Optic cup
- Future aqueduct of Sylvius
- Fourth ventricle
- Central canal

70 / Histogenesis of the Neural Tube

With the closure of the neural tube, the cells of the neural epithelium greatly expand. The epithelium is bounded on its luminal side by an internal limiting membrane, which is actually a basement membrane, and on its external side by an external limiting membrane. Cells actively proliferate by undergoing mitosis near the internal limiting membrane and remaining junctionally associated with the expanding neural epithelium. ■ **Fig. A** ■ As this process continues, the pseudostratified columnar epithelium of the neural tube becomes so thickened ■ **Fig. B** ■ that newly generated neuroblasts and glioblasts break away from the constraints of the epithelial boundary. As they do so, the cell bodies occupy a region just peripheral to the still-proliferating epithelium, where they undergo further histogenesis. Neuroblasts and glioblasts develop characteristic cell processes on the way to becoming fully differentiated cells. ■ **Fig. C** ■ Still peripheral to the cell bodies, processes are elaborated, many of which will become myelinated. At this point, three distinct zones of development are apparent: the inner, proliferative zone, called the ependymal layer; the intermediate zone, characterized by a preponderance of cell bodies, called the mantle layer; and the surrounding layer enriched in cell processes, the marginal layer.

This basic strategy is later modified throughout the developing central nervous system, especially in the brain. Populations of specific cell types migrate into the mantle zone and differentiate into characteristic strata or cell layers. This is clearly seen in the cerebellum ■ **Fig. D1** ■ and the cerebral cortex. ■ **Fig. D2** ■

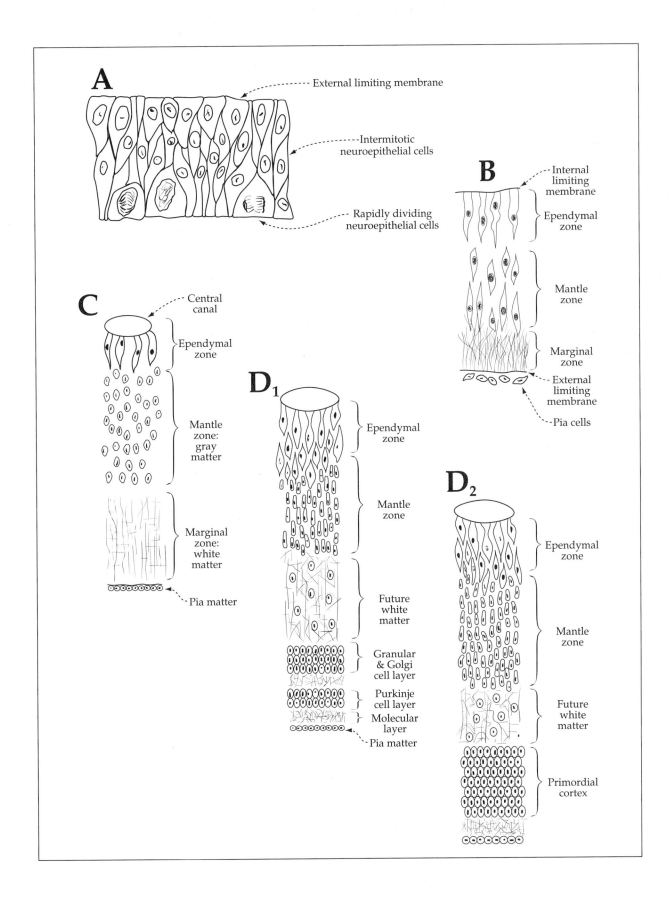

A
External limiting membrane
Intermitotic neuroepithelial cells
Rapidly dividing neuroepithelial cells

B
Internal limiting membrane
Ependymal zone
Mantle zone
Marginal zone
External limiting membrane
Pia cells

C
Central canal
Ependymal zone
Mantle zone: gray matter
Marginal zone: white matter
Pia matter

D₁
Ependymal zone
Mantle zone
Future white matter
Granular & Golgi cell layer
Purkinje cell layer
Molecular layer
Pia matter

D₂
Ependymal zone
Mantle zone
Future white matter
Primordial cortex

71 / Development of Motor and Sensory Components of the Central Nervous System

As the primitive neural tube expands, it differentiates both functionally and structurally. ■ **Fig. A** ■ At the level of the spinal cord, the central canal becomes elongated, still is lined by neuroepithelium, and spans the height of the neural tube from its dorsal side, the roof plate, to its ventral side, the floor plate. Near the center of the canal, a slight lateral expansion is evident. This is the sulcus limitans, which demarcates the basal lamina, or basal plate, lying ventral to it and the alar lamina, or alar plate, lying dorsally. The basal plate will be functionally segregated from the alar plate, the former giving rise to motor neurons and the latter to the sensory neurons. As development proceeds, these regions, composed primarily of cell bodies or gray matter, become further subdifferentiated into a complex of associated groupings, or nuclei. ■ **Fig. B** ■ By this time, the central canal has greatly diminished in relative size, and the spinal cord has developed a dorsal and ventral midline septum representing the obliteration of the central canal in these regions.

Although greatly modified, this same overall pattern can be appreciated as far rostrally as the hindbrain. ■ **Fig. C** ■ There the roof plate has been modified to form the thin-walled roof of the fourth ventricle and the sensory, or afferent, nuclei of the alar plate now take a lateral rather than a dorsal position. Similarly, the motor, or afferent, nuclei now are found medially rather than ventrally. This modification in relative position is due to the apparent flattening of the cylindrical spinal cord as the nuclei of the alar plate are forced laterally by the formation of the fourth ventricle. Specialized modifications such as this are characteristic of CNS embryology.

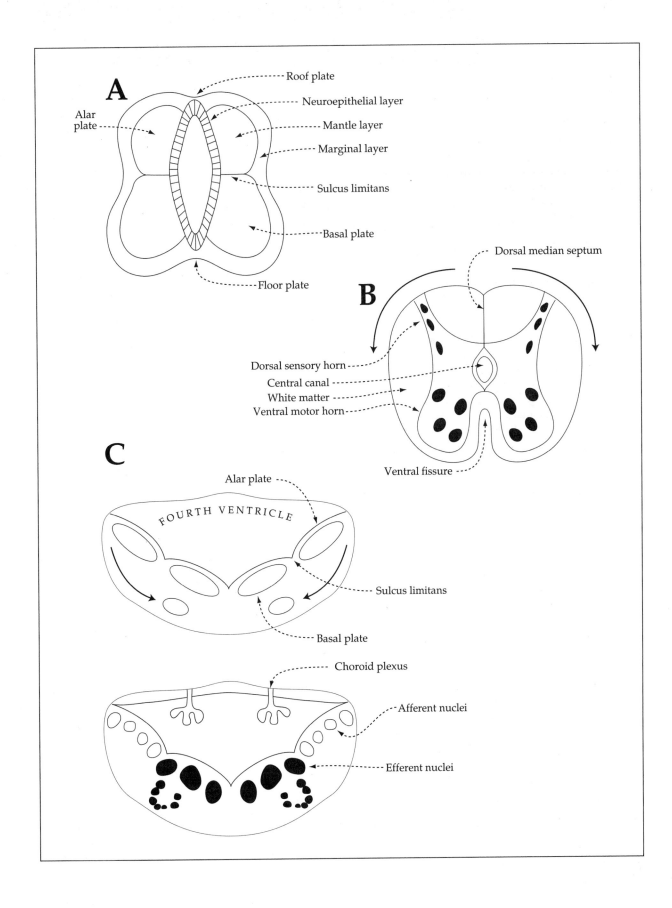

72 / Cell Lineages of Neurons and Neural Crest

The neuroepithelial cells that emerge from the neural tube contribute to two fundamental cell lineages. ■ **Fig. A** ■ The neuroblast line gives rise to the wide variety of differentiated neurons of the adult by specific cell migration, elaboration of cell processes, and acquisition of characteristic biochemical and physiologic properties. The glioblast lineage follows the same general developmental events to lead to oligodendocyte, astrocyte, and ependymal differentiation. The other major neuroglial element, the microglia, is thought to arise from a mesenchymal, not a neuroepithelial, precursor.

The neural crest cells (see Core Concept 7) give rise to an extremely broad and diverse set of differentiated cell types. From experimental evidence, it is clear that there are different developmental fates of the neural crest cells found in the head and neck region compared to the neural crest of the thoracic or trunk region. The rostral neural crest ■ **Fig. B** ■ contributes to the mesenchyme of the head and branchial arches and in particular to the visceral skeleton (see Core Concept 25).

The thoracic crest, as depicted in cross-section in ■ **Fig. C** ■, will contribute to the melanocytes found throughout the dermis; the sheath cells of Schwann, which envelop peripheral nerve cell axons; and the dorsal root (sensory) neurons, found parallel to the spinal cord. In addition, the wandering neural crest cells will form the neurons of the autonomic nervous system, which are found in association with the digestive system and accompanying blood vessels throughout the body. Because they are related to sympathetic neurons, the neural crest is also the precursor to the chromaffin cells of the adrenal medulla.

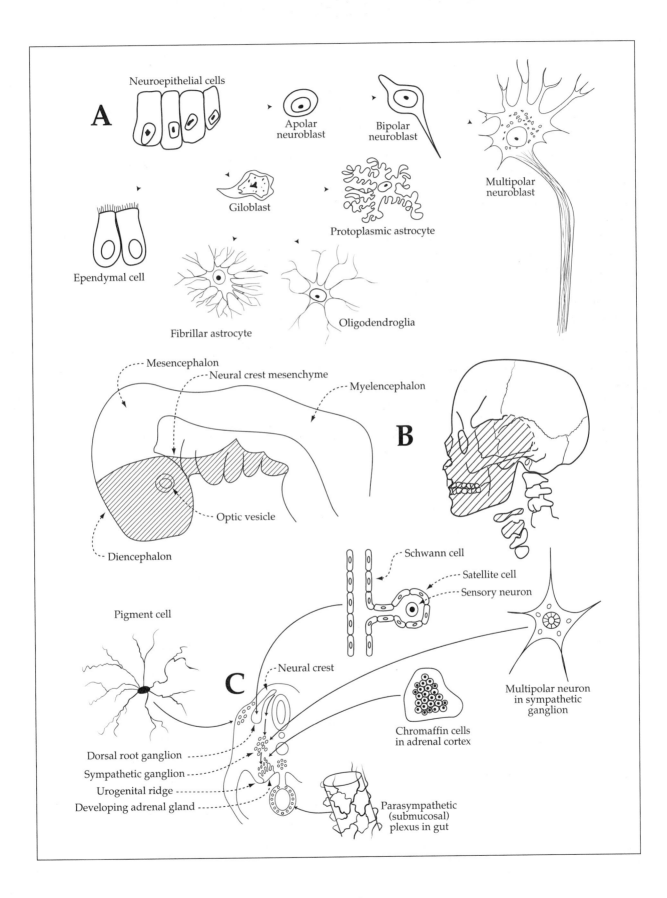

73 / Anomalies of Nervous System Development

For the CNS to develop normally, it is imperative that the vertebral column and the dura mater around the CNS also undergo proper development. A malformation in these elements may lead to a condition known as spina bifida. Spina bifida is a general term referring to a split in or incomplete differentiation of the dorsal spine involving osseous or nervous tissues, or both. Cranium bifidum refers to analogous anomalies of the skull.

In the most benign form of spina bifida, the vertebrae do not fully enclose the spinal cord, but without disruption of the nervous tissue. This anomaly is termed spina bifida occulta. ■ **Fig. A** ■ When the weakness of the vertebra allows the dorsal protrusion of dura mater with the saclike expansion of the cerebrospinal fluid–filled subarachnoid space, the resulting anomaly is called a meningocele. ■ **Fig. B** ■ A meningocele in which nervous tissue is disrupted from its normal position and found within the dorsal fluid–filled sac is a meningomyelocele. ■ **Fig. C** ■ Because of the involvement of nervous tissue, this anomaly is typically accompanied by severe neurologic deficits. In the most extreme case of spina bifida, failure of the neural tube to close at all in early development may leave the spinal cord open and uncovered. This condition is known as myeloschisis. ■ **Fig. D** ■

In the cranial region, the protrusion of a cerebrospinal fluid–filled cyst, often in the area of a fontanelle, is called a meningocele, just as is a similar protrusion of the spinal cord. ■ **Fig. E** ■ Such a protrusion accompanied by brain tissue is a meningoencephalocele. ■ **Fig. F** ■ When this anomaly also includes a portion of a brain ventricle within the cyst, it is termed a meningohydroencephalocele.

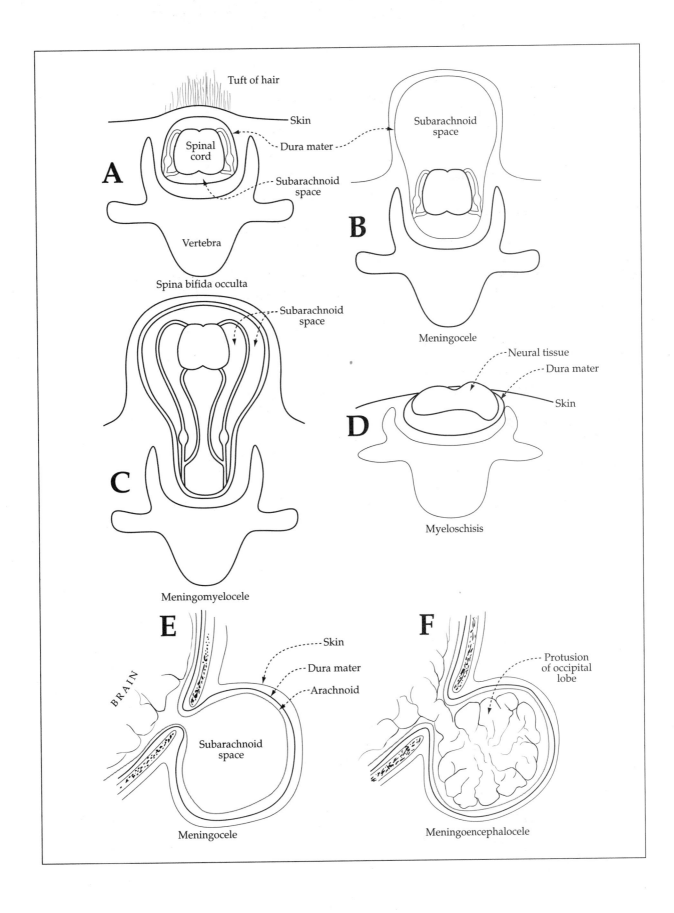

Tuft of hair

Skin

Spinal cord

Dura mater

Subarachnoid space

A

Vertebra

Spina bifida occulta

Subarachnoid space

B

Meningocele

Subarachnoid space

C

Meningomyelocele

Neural tissue

Dura mater

Skin

D

Myeloschisis

Skin

Dura mater

Arachnoid

BRAIN

E

Subarachnoid space

Meningocele

Protusion of occipital lobe

F

Meningoencephalocele

74 / Eye Development

By the fourth week of development, the newly formed neural tube displays bilateral diverticula at the level of the diencephalon. These lateral extensions of the future brain are the optic vesicles. ■ **Fig. A** ■ As each optic vesicle grows toward the surface ectoderm, it invaginates on itself to form a double-walled optic cup. ■ **Fig. B** ■ The inner layer of the optic cup develops into the pigmented retina, and the outer layer becomes the neural retina. The optic cup also induces the overlying surface ectoderm to form the lens by an invagination process that first results in a structure known as the lens vesicle. See ■ **Fig. B** ■ The optic cup is not a complete structure, but has a gap, or fissure, on its inferior border. ■ **Fig. C** ■ This optic fissure provides a passageway for the blood vessels (hyaloid artery and vein) that supply the developing eye. ■ **Figs. B and D** ■ By the end of the second month of development, the optic fissure closes off, enclosing the hyaloid vessels within the mesenchyme that formerly was found between the optic cup and the surface ectoderm. ■ **Fig. E** ■ The proximal portions of the hyaloid vessels become the central vessels of the retina when this surrounding mesenchyme is replaced by nerve axons growing from the diencephalon to the retina.

Since the eye is essentially an outgrowth of the brain, a dense, fibrous connective tissue sheath forms around the eyeball that is continuous with the dura mater of the optic nerve. This layer is called the sclera. ■ **Fig. F** ■ Anteriorly the sclera runs just deep to the surface ectoderm, and together they are induced by the underlying lens to differentiate into the cornea. Within the mesenchyme between the developing cornea and the lens, vacuoles appear. These vacuoles coalesce and become the anterior chamber of the eye. By midgestation a vascularized layer subjacent to the sclera appears. This is the choroid, which is continuous with the pia and arachnoid of the CNS. ■ **Fig. G** ■ The anterior advancement of the pigmented and neural epithelium develops into the iris. The ciliary muscles form from the underlying mesenchyme of the optic cup, and the pupillary muscles are derived from neural epithelium — a rare case where muscle develops from a nonmesodermal precursor.

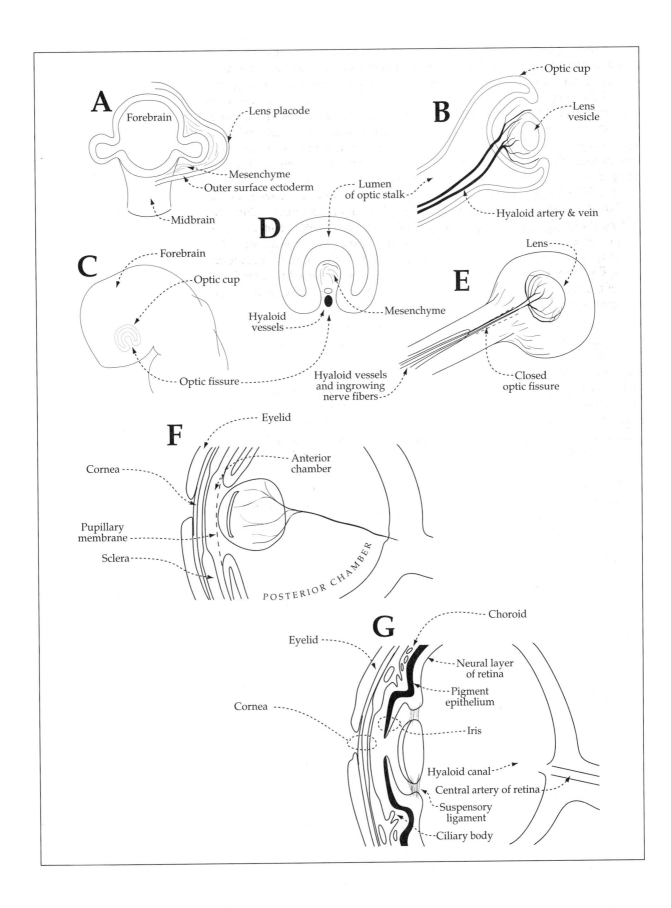

75 / Ear Development

The development of the external ear and the ear ossicles has been considered previously. The inner ear follows an embryologic sequence that may be traced to the otic vesicle. This structure begins as a bilateral thickening of the surface epithelium at the level of the hindbrain in the fourth week of development. Initially a pit forms ■ **Fig. A** ■, which invaginates below the surface ectoderm ■ **Fig. B** ■ and pinches off to become an isolated otic vesicle. ■ **Fig. C** ■

The otic vesicle undergoes a series of complex morphologic changes. Its superior portion becomes slightly dilated relative to the inferior part. These regions will develop into the utricle and saccule parts of the inner ear, respectively. In addition, a projection begins to grow medially out of the utricle region, which will elongate and form the endolymphatic duct. ■ **Fig. D** ■ The superior part of the otic vesicle continues to flatten and thin out to the point where central areas are absorbed away, leaving three interconnected ring-shaped structures arranged at approximately right angles to one another. At the same time, the inferior part of the otic vesicle begins to elongate, forming a spiral cochlear duct. ■ **Fig. E** ■ By midterm, the basic anatomy of the inner ear is established. ■ **Fig. F** ■ Sensory endings develop in dilations of the semicircular canals known as ampullae as well as in the utricle and saccule. Cells lining the cochlear duct will differentiate into the organ of Corti.

In cross section, the cochlear duct is lined by epithelium and surrounded by mesenchyme. ■ **Fig. G** ■ This mesenchyme will form the cartilaginous otic capsule (see Core Concept 20). As the capsule expands, vacuoles within the capsule develop and begin to coalesce. ■ **Fig. H** ■ The cochlear duct is finally positioned between these two perilymphatic spaces, the scala vestibuli and scala tympani, which are the result of the complete coalescence of these spaces. ■ **Fig. I** ■ Intrachondrial bone formation transforms the otic capsule into the bony labyrinth of the inner ear.

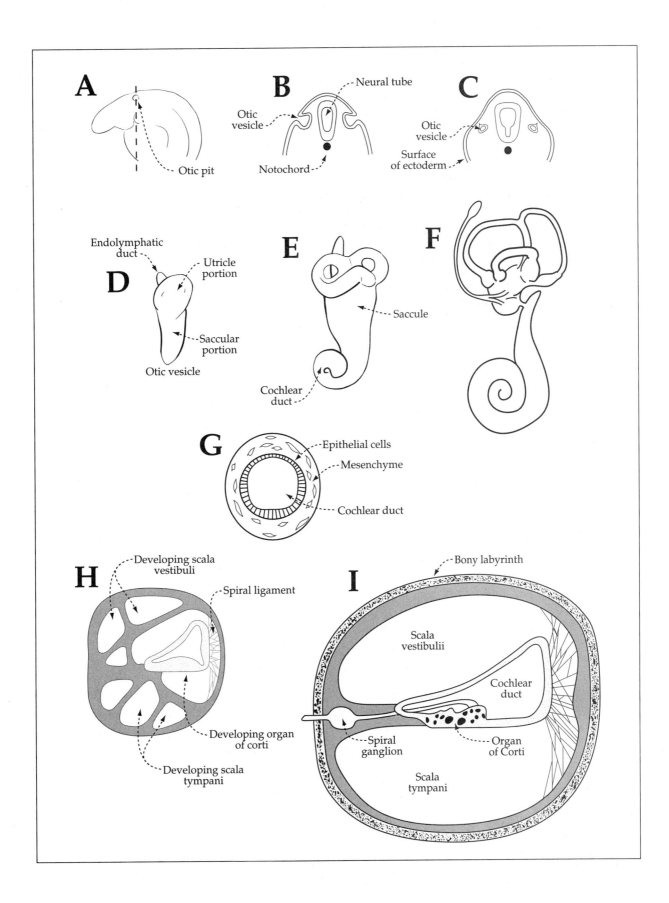

Index

Numbers followed by the letter *f* indicate figures.